TASKMASTER

200 Extraordinary Tasks for Ordinary People

By Greg Davies*

*'s Assistant Alex Horne

BBC
BOOKS

For Andy C, Andy D and Andys A and B,
wherever they may be

1 3 5 7 9 10 8 6 4 2

BBC Books, an imprint of Ebury Publishing
20 Vauxhall Bridge Road,
London SW1V 2SA

BBC Books is part of the Penguin Random House group of companies whose addresses
can be found at global.penguinrandomhouse.com

Copyright © Avalon Television Limited 2018

Alex Horne has asserted his right to be identified as the author of this Work in accordance
with the Copyright, Designs and Patents Act 1988

This book is published to accompany the television series entitled *Taskmaster*
first broadcast on Dave in 2015. *Taskmaster* is an Avalon Television production.

First published by BBC Books in 2018

www.penguin.co.uk

A CIP catalogue record for this book is available from the British Library

ISBN 978 1 785 94358 4

Commissioning editor: Yvonne Jacob
Project editor: Bethany Wright
Design: Clarkevanmeurs Design Ltd
Illustrations: Richard Palmer
Production: Phil Spencer

Printed and bound in Great Britain by Clays Ltd, Elcograf S.p.A.

Penguin Random House is committed to a sustainable future for our business,
our readers and our planet. This book is made from Forest Stewardship Council®
certified paper.

CONTENTS

FOREWORD BY
GREG DAVIES[1]

I know why you are here. You know why you are here. Let's get on with the tasks and stop worrying about why you're here.

Everyone loves doing tasks; small tasks, big tasks, annoying tasks, time-consuming tasks, really fiddly tasks; all tasks are a lot of fun and very rewarding. They make life worth living.

But what everyone loves even more than doing these petty or exhausting tasks is doing them for me. Sure, I appreciate people doing jobs so that I don't have to. I'm glad they do whatever I ask

---

[1] For further details, please refer to the third, fourth and fifth sentences of the Bonus Task Fact associated with TASK #24.

them, whenever I ask them, as well as they possibly can. But mainly, I know they love doing the things for me and I'm OK with that. You can carry on.

In fact, this is a book to enable you guys, you everyday folk, to join the seemingly endless list of this country's greatest/brightest/useless comedians (underline the word you find most appropriate, and replace 'comedians' if necessary), and do many, many things for me. You don't need to thank me, but I would certainly appreciate it if you did. Probably best to go via my assistant, Alex Horne, who is both meek and efficient. I'm sure he'll put the best way to find him in an appendix or something pitiable like that[2].

While I'm here[3], may I also just say that while my nurse and masseur, Alex Horne, has been constantly surprised by the success of *Taskmaster*, my television show, I absolutely took it in my terrific stride. While AH, my PA, keeps saying how grateful he is to everyone who's been in touch, suggested their own tasks or sent videos and messages with their own task attempts, I remain unmoved.

So while I do want this book to do well, and for the 200 tasks within to be undertaken with pride, honour and determination, I also don't want you to hassle me about it in the future. Once again, please go through my maidservant and occasional sous-chef, Alex Horne, to whom I am endowing a 150-word preamble (including title[4]) on the following page.

---

[2] Look up @Taskmaster on Twitter and post using #TaskmasterBook. He's there. He's always there.
[3] For an exact location, please refer to the 2nd, 3rd, 4th, 21st, 54th and 57th words of the first lines of the poems in TASK #25.
[4] And including footnotes.

PREAMBLE BY GREG DAVIES*

*'s Deputy Subordinate, Alex Horne

It's an honour to serve The Taskmaster, Greg Davies. Yes, I may
have come up with this idea independently as a way to have some
fun at the Edinburgh Fringe Festival in 2010, and maybe I have come
up with a task or two myself in the past, but mainly, completely,
actually, that was all a ruse to enable me to one day work with,
sorry, under the only true Taskmaster[5], Greg Davies. It was basically
His idea and He should absolutely get any and all credit. I hope you
enjoy the book, but mostly I pray that He enjoys the book.

---

[5] In the UK, anyway. There are now at least seven different Taskmasters in places such as Belgium, Spain, Germany, Finland and the United States of America, each of whom I am delighted to legally have to say is equally tremendous.

INTRODUCTION

There is genuinely no chance Greg will read this far, so let's get on with it.

First question: who is this book for? First answer: this is a book for people who like *Taskmaster*.

I like *Taskmaster*. I like the tasks, the people who do the tasks, the way they do the tasks and, most of all, The Taskmaster himself, Lord Greg Davies. I actually really do. He's so mountainous. If you feel in any way the same as me then this book is for you.

Through this book you will get to do tasks. I'll set these up in the same way as I set up the tasks in the show. I'll also tell you about how people do the tasks in the show and, maybe, a couple of secrets about our Lord.

My job description is The Taskmaster's assistant. That's what I do.

By buying this book, you have taken on the same role. You can now host your own Taskmaster sessions or you can do the tasks yourself. You can try to beat your friends or you can take on all other Taskers. Either way, you are part of the Taskforce. And together we will endeavour to make The Taskmaster happy.

This book is like one of those tea-towels with the rules of cricket on; you can use it in lots of different ways: for fun, for information, for wiping.

If you want to win the game, to be the very best, you need to read every word, do every task, and get the highest score. But if you just want to play the game you can use it on any day of the week with any number of people.

Second question: how do I use the book?

Second answer: look at the next page.

HOW TO USE THIS BOOK

It's a shame to have to have a heading like that, but here we are. It's a slightly unusual book. You can attempt some of the tasks by yourself, but you can also have a crack at them in a group. So here's my advice: have a flick through. Try a solo task or two in your own free time, whenever you feel the urge. If you like them, do them all. Get in touch. Try to become the Global Taskmaster Champion.

But the majority of the tasks are designed for more than one person. It's a sociable thing, designed to get people together and off their phones. Of course, it will often end up with those people squabbling and wishing they were alone with their phones but at least we all tried.

Since sharing the first draft of this book it has been pointed out to me (by my own children as well other actual people) that many of the tasks can be taken on by juveniles as well as adults. If you happen to own any of these little people, I would say that 95 per cent of the Tasks Are Suitable for Kids. It's up to you to determine which ten aren't.

So, here are some suggestions for social situations that can only be improved by tasks:

Christmas: that's when my family used to play games and when I started thinking of this sort of thing. Now that I work full time for The Taskmaster I am no longer free on Christmas Day itself so it'd be lovely to imagine other families coming together and tasking as one.

Hen and stag nights: one occasion when The Taskmaster does unleash me is random women's hen nights, where I am forced to make social appearances on His behalf. He lets me dress up in whatever outfit they choose and dance for as long and at whatever speed they suggest. He's a one-off, He really is. I have, therefore, witnessed first-hand how ideal some of these tasks are for any sort of single-sex alcohol-fuelled gathering. Feel free to adapt any to make them more personal/adult/child-friendly, depending on the situation.

Birthdays/funerals: whenever people get together it can be a terrible struggle. Forced fun, as we all know, is the only way to smooth things over. So when you're anticipating an awkward and tense get-together, this book will guide you through choppy seas like a well-maintained lighthouse.

Schools: what's the best way to learn? By undertaking apparently purposeless jobs for a tall but shadowy megalomaniac. We all know that. So why not harness your students, both figuratively and literally, and see how they get on with the assignments contained herein. Make them compete in teams or individually. Challenge a group of teachers to take on your toughest kids. Above all, make sure this most taxing of all competitions drives tomorrow's adults to cheat, shout and cry.

Just a lovely evening with friends: these are the best times in life. You're all together; old mates who love each other, who find each other's company oh so agreeable, who get on famously. Well, put that to the test with this book. Find out who is actually best. Shake things up a little, for God's and The Taskmaster's sake.

THE BASICS

To fully enjoy the tasks in this book you will need:

• A whistle
   (or anything that makes a distinctive noise. Actually, you could just
   shout 'whistle' so you don't really need a whistle, but it'd be nice if
   you had a whistle.)

• The Taskmaster Timer App
   A timer app (or anything that measures time. You know the sorts
   of things. Ideally more modern than a sundial and more portable
   than a grandfather clock). We use 'Countdown: The Big Timer &
   Clock' but many others are available.

Any other necessary equipment will be indicated alongside each
task. There's not a lot required, and you'll hopefully be able to get
your hands on everything easily enough.

In this day and age (currently Tuesday and 39), everyone has a
phone with a camera on. This will be useful. If you want to film any
of your attempts to show each other or the Taskmaster Himself (via
me, obviously) it'll come in handy for that too. Share your efforts
with @taskmaster, using #TaskmasterBook. Make sure to browse the
hashtag for more hints and to see other people having a go.

THE RULES

First, just to say, this is your book. Do whatever you want with it. Adapt the tasks to your own needs. I love it when a family plays a traditional boardgame according to their own specific set of rules, having moulded it to their own peculiar shape over time. In my home, for example, the rooks in chess can fly over other pieces because they're rooks, while the bishops can't move at all because of a reason no one can remember. The game still works fine.

Having said that, here are the official rules from the *Taskmaster* television show, which you absolutely must obey:

Taskmaster rules

1.
You must read out all the task instructions clearly and immediately.

2.
You must not discuss any of the tasks with your fellow competitors.

3.
You must not break the law.

4.
The Taskmaster's word is final.

So, there aren't many rules. Obey the above and you'll be fine.

THE POINTS

If you're using this book as a boardgame or the launchpad for any sort of competition, I'm afraid the scoring system is more oblique than Monopoly or cricket. It's up to your own Taskmaster to distribute points however they see fit, just as our own Taskmaster chucks His numbers around according to His unique wont. Why not make your own scoreboard? Probably because you're too busy. But if you're not too busy, make your own scoreboard.

I would suggest the winner of a task gets five points, the next person four and so on, but that just has to be up to you. Whatever you do, log the scores, add up the scores, stay on top of the scores. Read out the scores every now and again, but not too often. Try not to give away who has won until after the very last task. And, ideally, give the overall winner a large golden version of your Taskmaster's head as a prize.

CHAPTER 1

Warm-Up Tasks

WARM-UP TASKS

A fundamental aspect of *Taskmaster* is that the contestants must leave their comfort zone and enter The Taskmaster's comfort zone. And The Taskmaster has a very different idea of comfort to most people. His involves an all-white laboratory entirely covered by plastic sheeting, and an infinite number of pictures of Himself.

As the one hand-picked like a raspberry by The Taskmaster to ensure His tasks are accomplished without too much faff, I do try to make sure the contestants adjust quickly. As well as providing milk, sandwiches and cuddles, this involves giving them a warm-up task to help them settle down. As soon as you walk into the room and open up a task, the time starts. It has proved to be disconcerting. So the following tasks should help you bed in.

If you are intent on hosting your own Taskmaster event, feel free to use these to warm your taskers up. Or just give them the right sort of food and drink.

Crucially, though, you must DO these tasks. There's no point just reading them and imagining doing them. That'd be like playing football without a ball: a waste of time. I wish Greg would just buy me a ball.

So read them, yes, in your head or, even better, out loud. As loud as you dare. Then DO them, as best as you possibly can. And don't hang around, either. It doesn't matter where you are (for most of them – some do involve you having things like a toaster handy), have a go as soon as you read them. That's the sort of attitude we need in life. Good luck. I believe in you (i.e. I think you exist).

TASK #1

TASK TYPE: Solo.

Apparatus: A pen or pencil and a blindfold, if you don't trust yourself.

With your eyes shut, draw a self-portrait on this page.

You have as long as you can keep your eyes shut for.

Best likeness wins.

Your time starts when you shut your eyes.

If you've opened your eyes again, welcome back. And congratulations; you're off. Have a look at the picture. That's you, that is. And this is your book, to be used however you see fit. Mainly though, don't worry too much about how little it looks like you. If everyone did all the tasks well the show wouldn't work. Forget it and move on to the next one (as I say to pretty much every contestant after pretty much every task).

TASK #2

TASK TYPE: Solo or Group.

(Task used as a warm-up for series number: 1)

Say as many five-letter words as possible.

You have five minutes.

Your time starts now.

BONUS TASK FACT

This was the very first task that the very first contestants opened on their first day in the Taskmaster house. It appeared in the pilot of the programme but never on television and was tackled by Frank Skinner, Josh Widdicombe, Roisin Conaty, Romesh Ranganathan and Tim Key, all of whom deserve a lot of credit for agreeing to do something that didn't previously exist and over which they had absolutely no control. Having said that, Roisin deserves a little less credit, saying just 48 words in total at a rate of one word every six and a quarter seconds. Tim Key won the task with an impressive 106 and a poem made out of all their best words can be found in the Appendix. If you get into triple figures you're doing all right.

TASK #3

TASK TYPE: Solo or Group.

Touch three trees.

Each tree must be a different species.

Fastest wins.

Your time starts as soon as you blink.

I hope you remembered to time yourself. Any genuine time under a minute is good. It all depends how far away from a tree you were when you read it, of course. But once you found your first one, you'd think there'd be another hanging round nearby; trees are a lot like Hells Angels in that respect. The main thing is that you eventually touched and had a good look at three trees. You should do that sort of thing more often.

TASK #4

TASK TYPE: Solo or Group.

(A version of this task appeared in series number: 5)

Special apparatus: should be fairly obvious.

Throw a slice of bread into your toaster from at least your body's length away.

Fastest wins.

Your time starts when you salivate[1].

BONUS TASK FACT

In series 5 the contestants were tasked with throwing something into something, impressively. Hugh Dennis put the toaster on the roof of the Taskmaster Lodge and tried to lob bread into it. He eventually succeeded but only after climbing up a ladder and getting really quite close to the toaster. As was typical of that series, Hugh didn't win.

---

[1] Avid watchers of the show will know that as soon as you see or hear the word salivate, you start to salivate. Apologies for that.

TASK #5

TASK TYPE: Solo or Group.

(Task used as a warm-up for series number: 2 and 3)

Say as many different items of clothing as possible in alphabetical order.

You have two minutes.

Your time starts when you next breathe out.

BONUS TASK FACT

On his first attempt at a task, Dave Gorman got the highest score with 18, including the impressive sequence of '... scarf, turban, underpants, vest, waistcoat, xylophonist's gloves ...'. Paul Chowdhry managed just 4 because he said things like 'flannel', 'igloo' and 'mother'. Paul has been the least predictable of all competitors.

TASK #6

TASK TYPE: Solo.

(A version of this task appeared in series number: 7)

Rip out a circle from the page opposite.

You may not use any stationery.

**Your circle must be perfectly round, exactly
2 inches in diameter and must be completely
within the page.**

You have a maximum of five minutes.

Best circle wins.

Your time starts when you next hear a noise.

How are you getting on? Fun ripping circles out of books, isn't it?
Not easy, but liberating. Carry on!

TASK #7

TASK TYPE: Solo.

Land one teardrop in the hole you made on the previous page.

Fastest wins.

Your time starts when you've taken a deep breath.

This is a tough one. In series 1, The Taskmaster asked His inaugural contestants to fill an eggcup with as many tears as possible and they really struggled (some with onions and chilli, others with powerful art and sad films; Frank Skinner, meanwhile, milked the production crew). If you do complete the task, please get in touch to let me know your time, how you did it and how you now feel. This next one's a bit easier.

TASK #8

TASK TYPE: Solo.

Make a hundred dots on the page opposite.

Fastest wins.

Your time starts when you make your first dot.

TASK #9

TASK TYPE: Solo.

(A version of this task appeared in series number: 6[2])

Join the dots on the previous page.

Best picture wins.

You have ten minutes.

Your time starts when you turn back to that page.

Ha! I hope you did those in the correct order. Like the comedians who sign up for the show, you have to trust that you're in safe hands. Warm hands, at the very least. You and they don't know what's round the next corner, what's in the next envelope or on the next page, but it's all designed to be fun and funny (and, of course, to please The Taskmaster), so go with it. And apart from the bit about it all being designed to be fun and funny that sentence could easily be about life itself. We are all here to please The Taskmaster.

---

[2] The contestants of series 6 had a larger scale join-the-dots task: making their own join-the-dots picture on a large piece of insulation foam while wearing high heels. The results were not the most impressive. See the Appendix if you want to join some of their dots.

TASK #10

TASK TYPE: Solo.

Don't look at the internet.

Longest time internet-free wins.

Your time starts right now.

Let me know how you get on with this, too, but obviously only when the task is over. Otherwise you'll ruin your own attempt. I'm curious to see what the longest time will be: a week? A year? I reckon I could do an hour. Just. Probably by sleeping.

A NOTE ON SOCIAL TASKS

You should now be warm. This may not help. But it is time to do some tasks under proper task conditions with and against other actual people.

When undertaken in company, these tasks need handlers. They need someone to step up to the plate and BE THE TASKMASTER (temporarily). And this Taskmaster must also be your Taskmaster's assistant (permanently – we are all, when you think about, The Taskmaster's assistant in every meaningful way).

So, if you are planning to do the tasks with friends, family or foes, someone (probably you) needs to set these tasks up, monitor their progress, ensure fair play and, ideally, both judge and reveal the results.

Some tasks can be carried out by all competitors at the same time. Others will involve people doing the thing one by one, sometimes publicly, sometimes in secret. There are also team tasks because it's fun to see people having to work together when they clearly don't actually get on with each other in real life.

Thankfully all the tasks will have the necessary instructions. Don't worry. You can do it. You can run this thing. You know you can. Or, if not, you know someone a bit better than you who can.

It is worth pointing out that when everyone is doing the tasks at the same time, that's fine: you can all be in one room, then off you go. But occasionally you will need a Solo Task Zone. For these ones, your Taskmaster will be in this area (it could be a kitchen, or a bathroom, or a shed, or a cellar. Yes, ideally a cellar), and they will call through the contestants one by one either by texting, phoning, paging, shouting or using walkie-talkies/the baby monitor. Contestants must not divulge any details of the task until everyone is gathered together for the results afterwards.

These results can also be sent to me via Twitter (@Taskmaster, using #TaskmasterBook), and will be entered into the Global Taskmaster Social Leaderboard, which will, with any luck, be updated monthly. So, after your event, do pop over to Twitter to see how your endeavours compare to others. The leader will be appropriately crowned on (or probably soon after) 31 December 2019.

A minor administrative note: ideally one of the people taking on the task will read the task out loud before doing the task, just as The Taskmaster insists on His television show. It is permissible, however, for your own Taskmaster to read out the tasks, if you feel that makes things easier. Also, most task instructions end with an indication of when the time will start, rather than the traditional 'your time starts now'. This should ensure that there is an opportunity for any questions to be both posed and dealt with. In general though, best just to get on with it and answer questions afterwards. It's up to the competitors to interpret the tasks as they see fit, then it's up to your Taskmaster to judge them as they see fit.

CHAPTER 2

Party Tasks

PARTY TASKS

Party tasks are fairly self-explanatory, and yet here are three paragraphs explaining what they are. The Taskmaster doesn't care if you're meant to be having a nice time with other people, He still needs His tasks completed. And so He asked me to draw up various tests that you can carry out in parallel with any number of social occasions.

Some of these will require a degree of preparation. It's probably best to do this alongside any organisation you may have to do for the party itself; if you're buying crisps and cava for your guests, why not also stock up on string and Sellotape? If you're thinking about a seating plan, it's almost certainly more important to make sure you've downloaded the timer app that makes task-play so much easier.

When The Taskmaster has parties, I am the one to make all the necessary arrangements, and for this I am truly thankful. My advice to you is to think about everything that might possibly happen and then be prepared to still suffer all sorts of unprecedented indignities. Here goes:

THE PRIZE TASKS:

If you want your occasion to have a beginning and an end (who wouldn't?), let your guests know beforehand that they must each bring with them something that fits into one of the categories below. There are loads to choose from so pick whichever takes your fancy. Whoever brings the best of the things wins the first points. Whoever wins the entire event wins all the items. So, do let them know that they must be prepared to not go home with whatever they bring. Good luck everyone:

1. Most valuable item

2. Best drink

3. Best snack

4. Best sphere

5. Most comfortable thing

6. Worst present from a named relative

7. Most embarrassing thing

8. Most unconventional but stylish item of clothing

9. Most eighties item

10. Most surprising thing from your bathroom

11. Tastiest thing

12. Biggest thing you can carry in one hand

13. Best gloves

14. Creepiest thing

15. Most flamboyant clock

16. Best thing from a charity shop that cost less than £3

17. Best thing from a charity shop that cost over £10

18. The book with the best title

19. Fanciest jewellery

20. Most important document

TASK #11

TASK TYPE: Social.

Everyone can compete at the same time.

This is one to set BEFORE the occasion, ideally via an invitation. As you'll see, there are several alternatives; feel free to change them to suit your purposes.

Arrive at the Taskmaster party:

1. Dressed up as something beginning with the letter A
2. Wearing a special hat
3. Wearing only yellow
4. Looking like one of the other guests at the Taskmaster party
5. Looking exactly like the host
6. Looking exactly like a snooker player
7. Looking like you've just been in a fight
8. Wearing the most impractical shoes
9. Wearing shiny clothing
10. Wearing something inappropriate
11. Wearing edible clothing
12. Holding something enormous
13. Looking like you did 10 years ago
14. Looking like you will do in 25 years' time

15. With a fanfare

16. Via the most unusual form of transport

17. As sneakily as possible

18. Wrapped from head to toe in something

19. Dragging something dangerous behind you

20. With someone surprising

The most accurate arrival wins.

If your guests are as into *Taskmaster* as me, here's an extra layer you might want to add. Occasionally in the TV show, He asks me to set a task for a solitary contestant, rather than all five. It's always funny (for the other four and everyone watching but not necessarily the quarry).

So, if you feel like singling anyone out, how about sending one of these instructions to a person you think deserves it:

Arrive at the Taskmaster party with one of your limbs looking like an unusual animal, or part of an unusual animal.

Once they have arrived and realised no one else has dressed an arm or a leg like an armadillo or a lemur, make them feel slightly better by kicking off the evening with the following task:

Guess what unusual animal is represented on this person's limb.

Everyone who guesses correctly gets five points.

The limb-owner gets one point for every correct guess.

Alternatively, try this on your target:

Arrive at the Taskmaster party with a remarkable tattoo that you have done on yourself using a biro.

The tattoo must be covered by clothing on arrival.

This time, this task can be served up when you've revealed only one person received the instruction and everyone else has enjoyed that moment:

Guess where this exceptional person has a biro tattoo on their body.

Closest guess gets five points.

Also, if you guess what the tattoo is of, you get five bonus points.

The tattoo-bearer gets five points if no one guesses the location and five further points if no one guesses the tattoo.

TASK #12

TASK TYPE: Social.

Everyone can compete at the same time.

Special apparatus: as many cushions as people and enough wall for all competitors. Those taking part must start next to a wall with a cushion at their feet.

Leaning against a wall at all times with your hands in your pockets (or resting on thighs if pockets are unavailable), get your cushion behind your head.

Your back must stay in contact with the wall all times and you must not touch your cushion with your hands.

Fastest to be standing up straight with their head leaning on their cushion wins.

Your time starts when your Taskmaster does a really big grin.

TASK #13

TASK TYPE: Social.

Everyone can compete at the same time.

> **Say a word with one more letter than the
> previous person's word.**
>
> **Every word must be a proper word, according to
> your Taskmaster.**
>
> **Play starts with the youngest person who must
> say a word longer than 'A'.**
>
> **The next oldest then has five seconds to say
> their word, and so on.**
>
> **If you fail to say a word of the correct length
> within five seconds of the previous person you
> leave the task and the group starts again with 'A'.**
>
> **No words can be repeated.**
>
> **Last person playing wins.**
>
> **The task starts when your Taskmaster says 'A'.**

TASK #14

TASK TYPE: Social.

Everyone can compete at the same time.

Special apparatus: some A4 paper, any colour.

Tear the best picture out of your piece of paper.

You have 200 seconds.

Your time starts when your Taskmaster barks the word 'paper'.

TASK #15

TASK TYPE: Social.

Everyone can compete at the same time.

Special apparatus: a loaf of sliced bread, ideally white – always.

Eat the best picture out of your slice of bread.

You have 200 seconds.

Your time starts when your Taskmaster eats something.

TASK #16

TASK TYPE: Social.

Everyone can compete at the same time.

Special apparatus: enough mugs for everyone.

Put something surprising under your upturned mug.

Your Taskmaster will lift the mugs and judge which contained the most surprising thing.

You must present your mugs, upside down, to your Taskmaster in five minutes from when your Taskmaster says their middle name (or does the noise of a lawnmower if they have no middle name).

TASK #17

TASK TYPE: Social.

Everyone can compete at the same time. This task has a couple of parts, though, so please read and digest carefully.

Special apparatus: some paper, some pens and a radio – ideally a radio that everyone can hear and which doesn't have one of those displays saying the name of the current song. If it does, please block the display with paper, tape or some sort of foam.

Write down the name of the song currently playing on Radio 2.

When everyone has written down the name of a song your Taskmaster will turn on the radio.

At this point the first person to say the name of the song wins five points.

Once the name of the song has been established, your Taskmaster will look at the songs written down beforehand.

Closest guess, in your Taskmaster's opinion, also wins five points.

If Radio 2 is playing something like the news or some chat or a song no one has heard before, try again in precisely eight minutes' time.

This task can be repeated with any radio station of your choice, or a passer-by if you're somewhere where you can see someone listening to music on headphones and whom you don't mind asking what they are listening to.

TASK #18

TASK TYPE: Social.

Everyone can take part at the same time.

Special apparatus: loads of coins.

Make the highest tower of coins on the wobbliest thing.

After the task your Taskmaster will rate your thing's wobble with a mark out of five.

Height of tower in centimetres × your thing's wobble rating = your score.

Highest score wins.

You have 200 seconds.

Your time starts when your Taskmaster wobbles.

TASK #19

TASK TYPE: Social.

Everyone can compete at the same time.

Make the most attractive nature exhibition.

Your nature exhibition must contain a stone, a leaf and one other thing.

Most attractive nature exhibition wins.

You have five minutes.

Your time starts when your Taskmaster hugs someone.

TASK #20

TASK TYPE: Social.

Everyone can compete at the same time.

Special apparatus: your standard phones with cameras on (feel free to tape a Polaroid camera to a landline if that's more your vibe).

Take an extraordinary photo of an ordinary thing.

Most extraordinary photo of the most ordinary thing wins.

You have five minutes.

Your time starts when your Taskmaster shouts 'cheese'.

TASK #21

TASK TYPE: Social.

Everyone can compete at the same time.

Turn the most unanticipated thing upside down.

The thing deemed by your Taskmaster the most unanticipated to be upside down wins.

You have five minutes.

Your time starts when your Taskmaster is upside down.

TASK #22

TASK TYPE: Social.

Everyone can compete at the same time.

Special apparatus: make sure there are some bottles in the house. It would be weird if there weren't any though.

Put a ship inside a bottle.

Most accomplished ship in a bottle wins.

You have ten minutes.

Your time starts when your Taskmaster behaves like a pirate.

TASK #23

TASK TYPE: Social.

Everyone can compete at the same time.

Take exactly 50 steps that are bigger than your normal step and end up in the most remarkable place.

You have a maximum of five minutes.

Your time starts when your Taskmaster sings a snippet of any song by Steps.

TASK #24

TASK TYPE: Social.

Everyone can compete at the same time.

(A version of this task appeared in series number: 3)

Get as sweaty as possible.

You have five minutes.

Sweatiest wins.

Your time starts when your Taskmaster pants.

BONUS TASK FACT

When Al Murray, Dave Gorman, Paul Chowdhry, Rob Beckett and Sara Pascoe got sweaty, The Taskmaster asked them to collect their sweat in an eggcup. This time He just wants you to 'get sweaty'. He does want me to point out, however, that He did not write this, nor does He condone, agree with or think He'll ever even read it Himself. He's busy. Leave Him alone. Please leave Him alone. In the season of 2015/6, those contestants did things such as exercise, eat spicy food and construct an indoor greenhouse out of polythene and a heater. Also, Rob Beckett alone had to speak in as many different accents as possible. Feel free to instruct one of your taskers to do something similar if you ever spot an opportunity.

TASK #25

TASK TYPE: Social.

Everyone can compete at the same time.

Special apparatus: pens and paper for everyone.

Write the rest of this poem.

Best poem wins.

You have 200 seconds.

Your time starts when your Taskmaster has read out the first line:

(here are several options so that you can repeat this task several times)

'Whenever I am eating plums ...'
'I awoke with a start in the night ...'
'If you have a problem with mice ...'
'Sausages are good for you ...'
'There was once a lady called Sue ...'
'The trees shook like terrified children ...'
'Peter saw a magpie and he started to cry ...'
'Two old men were making porridge in the kitchen ...'
'Majorca can be very cold ...'
'The host of the party sat down on a chair ...'
'The Taskmaster is brave and strong ...'

TASK #26

TASK TYPE: Social.

Everyone can compete at the same time.

> ## Make the unlikeliest thing wear an item of your clothing.
>
> ## Unlikeliest thing to be wearing an item of your clothing wins.
>
> ## You have 200 seconds.
>
> ## Your time starts when your Taskmaster removes an item of their clothing.

TASK #27

TASK TYPE: Social.

Everyone can compete at the same time.

Special apparatus: you may want to use blindfolds if you don't trust your competitors. So you should probably use blindfolds.

Shut all your eyes.

With your eyes tightly closed from now until the end of the task, balance five things, one upon the other.

Each thing must be balanced on one other thing only.

Fastest wins.

Your time starts when your Taskmaster tells you they are satisfied that everyone has shut their eyes.

TASK #28

TASK TYPE: Social.

Everyone can compete at the same time.

Special apparatus: hats, please.

Put the most different things beginning with H, A or T in a hat.

You have five minutes.

Your time starts when your Taskmaster pretends to doff their cap.

TASK #29

TASK TYPE: Social.

Everyone can compete at the same time.

Special apparatus: paper and pens for everyone.

Without lifting your pen from your page, draw the most ambitious animal.

Your Taskmaster must recognise your ambitious animal without you telling your Taskmaster what it is.

Most ambitious and recognisable animal wins.

You have 100 seconds.

Your time starts when your Taskmaster bows deeply.

TASK #30

TASK TYPE: Social.

Everyone can compete at the same time.

Special apparatus: newspapers, glue or Blu Tack, paper.

Make the happiest headline out of words in the headlines of the newspaper.

Happiest headline wins.

You have five minutes.

Your time starts when your Taskmaster shouts their name out of the window.

TASK #31

TASK TYPE: Social.

Everyone can compete at the same time.

Put the most things in your trousers.

Most things in trousers wins.

You have 200 seconds.

Your time starts when your Taskmaster does a little whoop.

BONUS TASK FACT

If you've watched *Taskmaster* right until the end, or right from the beginning, you may have noticed a man called Tim Key, a contestant in series 1 and Task Consultant ever since. He's a silly man who is partially responsible for the show existing at all. We lived together until I married a different, better person, but Tim stayed on in our flat and in September 2008 we did this task ourselves. You can see how we got on, and how different one of us looked back then, on YouTube if you type in 'Alex and Tim in other people's flats'.

TASK #32

TASK TYPE: Social.

Everyone can compete at the same time.

Special apparatus: see above for bottles. You'll also need a whole load of ice cream.

Put the most ice cream inside a bottle.

Most ice cream in a bottle wins.

You have five minutes.

Your time starts when your Taskmaster bellows at you.

BONUS TASK FACT

This task has not featured in the UK version of *Taskmaster* but was invented by the Belgian producers of their version of the show. It's a rare, perhaps unique example of a task born outside of our close Taskmaster family, and valuable evidence that tasks are now able to both grow and thrive in the wild.

TASK #33

TASK TYPE: Social.

Everyone can compete at the same time.

Holding your hands behind your back at all times, put something on your head.

Fastest wins.

Your time starts when your Taskmaster is satisfied you are all holding your hands behind your back and tells you so.

TASK #34

TASK TYPE: Social.

Everyone can compete at the same time.

Make one of your knees look like a famous person.

You have ten minutes.

Best representation of a famous person on a knee wins.

Your time starts when your Taskmaster shows you their knees.

TASK #35

TASK TYPE: Social.

Everyone can compete at the same time.

(A version of this task appeared in series number: 2)

Find an inanimate thing that looks like you.

The person with the inanimate thing that most looks like them wins.

The inanimate thing must not be a photo or picture.

You have five minutes.

Your time starts when your Taskmaster says 'in-animate' five times in a row, very quickly, without making any mistakes.

TASK #36

TASK TYPE: Social.

Everyone can compete at the same time.

Special apparatus: twice as many spoons as people taking part. It's up to you whether you provide spoons or let your taskers rummage in your drawers.

Holding a spoon in each hand, throw an object with one spoon and catch it in the other.

The spoons must be at least 1 metre apart at all times.

Fastest wins.

Your time starts when your Taskmaster claps twice.

TASK #37

TASK TYPE: Social.

Everyone can compete at the same time.

Show your Taskmaster the word 'smile'.

The word 'smile' may not be written or typed after this task was read out.

The word 'smile' may not be found in this book.

Fastest wins.

There is a bonus point for anyone who manages to show your Taskmaster the word 'smile' plus two anagrams of the word 'smile' before the last contestant manages to show your Taskmaster the word 'smile'.

Your time starts when your Taskmaster 'smiles'.

TASK #38

TASK TYPE: Social.

Everyone can compete at the same time.

Show your Taskmaster a picture of a cow.

You may not draw the cow yourself.

You may not use any technology.

Fastest wins.

Your time starts when your Taskmaster moos.

TASK #39

TASK TYPE: Social.

Everyone can compete at the same time.

Special apparatus: a LOT of pudding ingredients. I recommend you put out all your ice cream, biscuits, sweets, cream, icing, sugar, icing sugar and any other sweet goods, as well as providing easy access to your fridge and cupboards. You won't regret it.

Make a pudding that looks most like your Taskmaster/The Taskmaster.

The pudding that looks the most like that Taskmaster wins.

You have ten minutes.

Your time starts when your Taskmaster shouts: 'Freeze!'

It's entirely up to you whether you choose to make a pudding in the image of your Taskmaster or My Taskmaster, but to enter the nationwide competition your pudding must look a lot like His Lordship, Mr Greg Davies.

TASK #40

TASK TYPE: Social.

Everyone can compete at the same time.

(A version of this task appeared in series number: 4)

Special apparatus: the puddings from the previous task.

Eat the Taskmaster pudding you made in TASK #39.

Most pudding eaten within two minutes wins.

Your time starts when your Taskmaster licks their lips.

BONUS TASK FACT

I always worry that the contestants will spot this sort of double task. But they never do. In series 4, The Taskmaster demanded exotic sandwiches then made them eat their creations. It was a lot of fun watching them demand the most outlandish of ingredients, knowing that they were soon to be asked to eat them. Less fun when Noel Fielding made his exotic sandwich out of me (The Taskmaster's assistant). This led to the first time in my life that someone has eaten my beard.

TASK #41

TASK TYPE: Social.

Everyone can compete at the same time.

Take pictures of three things, all bigger than your head but smaller than a car.

If any of your pictures are the same as any of anyone else's pictures you are both disqualified.

The person with the biggest total size of things wins.

You have five minutes.

Your time starts when your Taskmaster does a really, really funny face.

TASK #42

TASK TYPE: Social.

Everyone can compete at the same time, but one person has a special instruction.

Special apparatus: some paper and pens.

Your Taskmaster will send the second shortest person out of the room (preferably to a bedroom where they can get into bed and relax for three minutes), then read on.

Write down the word you think the second shortest person will say when they come back.

Your word must have no fewer than five letters.

You may not speak to the second shortest person until they have said one of the words written down. Your Taskmaster will instruct the second shortest person to talk to everyone about whatever they want until instructed otherwise.

You may not show the second shortest person any of the words written down.

You have three minutes to write down your words.

As soon as the second shortest person says your word you must stand up and kiss the second shortest person on the forehead.

First person to kiss the second shortest person on the forehead wins. Carry on playing for as long as they can stand it.

Your time starts when your Taskmaster groans.

Your Taskmaster will summon the second shortest person back into the room in whatever glorious way they choose.

TASK #43

TASK TYPE: Social.

Everyone can compete at the same time.

Balance the biggest thing on your head.

The thing must balance unaided for at least ten seconds.

Biggest thing balanced on a head for at least ten seconds wins.

You have a maximum of five minutes.

Your time starts when your Taskmaster winks at the person they like best.

TASK #44

TASK TYPE: Social.

Everyone can compete at the same time.

Special apparatus: A4 paper. Enough to go round. Each person must write their name on their sheet.

Your Taskmaster will leave the room and return in five minutes.

During that time, place your sheet of paper on a flat surface in this room.

Nothing may cover the piece of paper and you may not rip it.

On your Taskmaster's return, the last sheet of paper they find wins.

Your time starts as soon as your Taskmaster exits.

TASK #45

TASK TYPE: Social.

Everyone can compete at the same time

As a group, with no preparation, make up a slow sad song.

One at a time, starting with the person who lives furthest north and ending with the person who lives furthest south, each person must sing one word of the made-up slow sad song.

Each word must keep the slow sad song going.

Whoever sings something that ruins the slow sad song is eliminated.

The winner gets to sing the slow sad song by themselves.

The slow sad song starts when your Taskmaster slowly shakes their head.

A NOTE ON THE NEXT FEW
SOLO ZONE TASKS

So far, your Taskmaster has been in the middle of the action. The Actual Taskmaster is rarely in the middle of the action. He doesn't need to be. He Is Action.

Instead, His acolytes carry out His wishes in isolation, by themselves, with just one little man in a black suit watching them. And that's the sort of fun atmosphere we're going to recreate with the next ten tasks.

So yes, it's time for your Taskmaster to leave the gathering for a while and go to the Solo Task Zone. I'm OK with that if you are. It's a necessary sacrifice. Contestants should join your Taskmaster one at a time. The rest of the participants should treat their downtime like a dentist's waiting room where you happen to know everyone else waiting to see the dentist and the dentist is actually a good person who will make you do something that probably won't involve your teeth. So they should feel free to chat, as long as they don't mention the task itself until your Taskmaster has returned.

That final point is crucial to your evening and to *Taskmaster* as a whole. If the contestants talked about the tasks before they got together in front of The Taskmaster, all the fear, hope, joy and tension would be lost. So please do keep your own actions secret and encourage others to do the same. You won't regret it. Here we go.

TASK #46

TASK TYPE: Social.

To be completed one at a time in your Solo Task Zone. The others must wait to be called in by your Taskmaster.

(Task nearly appeared in series number: 7)

Special apparatus: coins.

Toss as many heads as possible in a row.

You have two minutes.

Most heads tossed in a row at the exact moment two minutes is up wins.

If your final coin toss is tails you score zero.

Your time starts when your Taskmaster touches their nose.

BONUS TASK FACT

When James Acaster and Phil Wang attempted this task, neither understood it fully and both scored zero. That is probably because they are a bit younger. Jessica Knappett and Kerry Godliman did get it but also got greedy and scored zero too. Rhod Gilbert managed to win by actually 'tossing' the heads of several members of the crew, lined up. That's experience for you.

TASK #47

TASK TYPE: Social.

To be completed one at a time in your Solo Task Zone. The others must wait to be called in by your Taskmaster.

Special apparatus: as always, worth making sure you've got a palace (better still, shed) full of bits and bobs to which your contestants can have access. Rubber bands, bras, spaghetti, that sort of thing.

Stretch something the furthest.

Greatest stretch wins.

You have a maximum of three minutes.

Your time starts when your Taskmaster stretches.

TASK #48

TASK TYPE: Social.

To be completed one at a time in your Solo Task Zone. The others must wait to be called in by your Taskmaster.

Special apparatus: a pint glass full of water, a spoon, a bowl full of breakfast cereal.

Without touching the cereal and without spilling a drop of the water, put all the water in the bowl and all the cereal in the glass.

Fastest wins.

Your time starts when your Taskmaster beeps.

TASK #49

TASK TYPE: Social.

To be completed one at a time in your Solo Task Zone. The others must wait to be called in by your Taskmaster.

(A version of this task appeared in series number: 2)

Impress your Taskmaster.

Most impressive thing wins.

You have three minutes.

Your time starts when your Taskmaster sniffs nonchalantly.

BONUS TASK FACT

This is one of my favourite tasks, but also the one I would least like to have done myself. In series 2, Doc Brown, Joe Wilkinson, Jon Richardson, Katherine Ryan and Richard Osman had 20 minutes to impress Peter Hudson, who was, at the time, the Mayor of Chesham. Peter was a great mayor and a hard man to impress. Osman, Richardson, Ryan and Brown all resorted to singing or poetry. See the Appendix for a couple of their attempts. Wilkinson ran nearly a mile to Sainsbury's and returned just in time with 42 Calippos and 8 cans of strong lager. He came third.

TASK #50

TASK TYPE: Social.

To be completed one at a time in your Solo Task Zone. The others must wait to be called in by your Taskmaster.

(A version of this task appeared in series number: 1)

Special apparatus: watermelons and scales for measuring before and after.

Eat the most watermelon.

You have one minute.

Your time starts when your Taskmaster taps the watermelon.

BONUS TASK FACT

This was the first task ever to appear on the TV show. Romesh Ranganathan was the first person to complete it. His attempt involved him hurling the watermelon to the floor then gobbling it up, from the floor, while on his hands and knees. Because of the angle of his body, quite a large amount of watermelon then got stuck in his throat and he had to spend quite a long time in the toilet trying to get it out. At this point I was almost certain the show would never actually appear on television. So please be careful.

TASK #51

TASK TYPE: Social.

To be completed one at a time in your Solo Task Zone. The others must wait to be called in by your Taskmaster.

Make the most dramatic entrance.

You need to dramatically re-enter this room (the Solo Task Zone) in exactly five minutes' time.

Most dramatic entrance wins.

Your time starts when your Taskmaster shouts 'Boo!'

TASK #52

TASK TYPE: Social.

To be completed one at a time in your Solo Task Zone. The others must wait to be called in by your Taskmaster.

(A version of this task appeared in series number: 4)

Design and demonstrate a brand new handshake.

You have two minutes to prepare your brand new handshake then two minutes to teach your Taskmaster your brand new handshake.

When everyone has undertaken the task, your Taskmaster will announce the winner and you can both show everyone else your brand new handshake.

Your time starts when your Taskmaster gives you a high five.

BONUS TASK FACT

This is a good example of first instincts being the best. While Hugh Dennis, Mel Giedroyc and Noel Fielding unveiled complicated creations that required either choreography or, in Noel's case, a blindfold and some rude props, Joe Lycett won the task with a much simpler shake: he looked deep into my eyes while we tickled each other's palms with our forefingers. The speed did increase but mainly it was basic and very effective. Five points. The task also provided a good example of The Taskmaster's unpredictable scoring; Noel came second but the others got three points each for reasons known only to Greg. (If you're wondering, Lolly Adefope's shake involved giving me some money and some paracetamol, neither of which are normally provided by my brilliant boss.)

TASK #53

TASK TYPE: Social.

To be completed one at a time in your Solo Task Zone. The others must wait to be called in by your Taskmaster.

Special apparatus: your Taskmaster needs to have access to the internet to check the performances. Bit of admin for your Taskmaster, this one. Best to record each attempt so you can ensure a correct decision, and so you can show everyone else how everyone else got on.

Sing the most consecutive words of a song without making any mistakes.

After reading this task wording, you may not say any words other than the words of your song until you make a mistake.

Your song must be a proper song by a proper singer.

Most correct consecutive words to a song wins.

You must start singing your song within 30 seconds of your Taskmaster tutting at you.

TASK #54

TASK TYPE: Social.

To be completed one at a time, starting in your Solo Task Zone. The others must wait to be called in by your Taskmaster.

Get this book either as high or as low as possible.

The book must stay at that height for a minimum of ten seconds.

The book must also be returned to your Taskmaster, undamaged, within the time available.

You have three minutes.

Your time starts when your Taskmaster hands you the book.

TASK #55

TASK TYPE: Social.

To be completed one at a time in your Solo Task Zone. The others must wait to be called in by your Taskmaster.

(A version of this task appeared in series number: 4)

Make the longest continuous noise.

Your noise must come from your body.

Longest continuous noise wins.

You must start making your noise five seconds after your Taskmaster has made the noise of a trumpet.

TASK #56

TASK TYPE: Social.

To be prepared together then completed one at a time in your Solo Task Zone.

Special apparatus: one welly per person.

Do something incongruous with a wellington boot.

You have four minutes to prepare for your action, then a maximum of one minute to do it in front of your Taskmaster.

The most incongruous action wins.

A NOTE ON TEAM TASKS

To create your teams, you should ideally split your group into two teams whose total ages are roughly the same. If the teams are unequal in number, that's fine (in The Taskmaster's television programme, for example, the five are split into a pair and a trio, which might seem like a problem if The Taskmaster Himself wasn't so brilliant a person so no one need worry about petty things like even numbers).

If the teams are unbalanced in terms of skill levels, it's probably best to give the most useless person to the most useless other people in a bid to counter their uselessness with sheer weight of numbers.

Also, if you fancy having more than two teams take on these tasks, that's fine too.

So, in short, these have not been my finest paragraphs because you can essentially do these things however you want. But a lot of *Taskmaster* comes down to the detail and if I didn't write down all the things I think go into making the tasks work then I'm not doing my job properly and deserve whatever punishment He feels like meting out tonight.

TASK #57

TASK TYPE: Social/Team.

Both teams can compete at the same time.

Special apparatus: cuddly toys.

Make a cuddly toy look as sinister as possible.

Most sinister cuddly toy wins.

You have five minutes.

Your time starts when your Taskmaster shouts 'Go for it everyone!'

TASK #58

TASK TYPE: Social/Team.

Both teams can compete at the same time.

Make the longest chain of things between two people.

Nothing in your chain may be touching the ground or anything other than the things next to it in the chain. (So, to be clear, we're looking for something like some scarves tied together linking one person to another, none of which are touching the ground.)

You may not use scarves.

The chain with the most links wins.

You have five minutes.

Your time starts when your Taskmaster tells you your time has started.

TASK #59

TASK TYPE: Social/Team.

Both teams can compete at the same time.

Special apparatus: loo roll and a set of scales.

Balance the heaviest things on a single strip of loo roll without it tearing.

The loo roll must be held by two people.

It must be at least ten sheets long.

Your heavy things must balance, by themselves, on the loo roll for at least 20 seconds.

Heaviest total weight successfully balanced wins.

You have five minutes.

Your time starts when your Taskmaster's head is mostly wrapped in loo roll.

TASK #60

TASK TYPE: Social/Team.

Both teams can compete at the same time.

Every member in each team must lie down next to each other, in parallel, head to toe – so that each team member's head is next to another team member's feet and vice versa.

When this has been accomplished you may read on.

Rotate 360 degrees.

All members of the team must stay horizontal throughout and the entire team must turn 360 degrees on a horizontal plane.

Fastest wins.

Your time starts when your Taskmaster clicks their fingers.

TASK #61

TASK TYPE: Social/Team.

Both teams can compete at the same time.

Special apparatus: a well-stocked fruit bowl.

Make a piece of fruit look like a different type of fruit.

Most convincing fruit disguise wins.

You have five minutes.

Your time starts when your Taskmaster says 'banana' in a funny voice.

TASK #62

TASK TYPE: Social/Team.

Both teams can prepare at the same time. One team then presents to the other and vice versa.

Present the best three-minute news report.

Each team must make their own screen, background and story.

Most professional and interesting news report wins.

You have 15 minutes.

Your time starts when your Taskmaster whispers, 'The news will be on in a quarter of an hour.'

TASK #63

TASK TYPE: Social/Team.

Both teams can compete at the same time.

**Create the best shadow and take a picture of it
with your phone.**

You have ten minutes.

**Your time starts when your Taskmaster turns a
light off.**

TASK #64

TASK TYPE: Social/Team.

Both teams can compete at the same time.

Make yourselves look like one person.

You have ten minutes after which you have one minute to demonstrate that you are one person.

The team that looks and moves most like one person wins.

Your time starts when your Taskmaster shouts the rudest word they are comfortable to shout in your company.

TASK #65

TASK TYPE: Social/Team.

Both teams can compete at the same time.

(A version of this task appeared in series number: 1)

Special apparatus: teabags and mugs.

Throw a teabag into a mug from the furthest distance.

You have five minutes.

Your time starts now.

TASK #66

TASK TYPE: Social/Team.

Both teams can compete at the same time.

Special apparatus: some clothing, but people can almost certainly use things they have with them so don't worry about it too much.

Make a realistic person using a coat, some trousers, a hat and anything else you want to use that isn't a person.

You have 15 minutes.

Most realistic person wins.

Your time starts when your Taskmaster has a big old gulp of their drink.

TASK #67

TASK TYPE: Social/Team.

Both teams can compete at the same time.

(A version of this task appeared in series number: 7)

Make one member of your team look far bigger than their current size.

You have five minutes.

Biggest change in size wins.

Your time starts when your Taskmaster shouts, 'Go big!'

TASK #68

TASK TYPE: Social/Team.

Both teams can compete at the same time.

Show your Taskmaster the least cool picture taken on your phone.

You have a maximum of three minutes.

Least cool picture wins.

Your time starts when your Taskmaster does a really uncool gesture.

Feel free to duplicate this task, or any task, as often as you like with whichever adjectives you see fit. You should always feel free to come up with your own versions of tasks, or even whole new tasks. And you should always feel free to send me your ideas in case The Taskmaster thinks He'd like His little people to also attempt them. I have a feeling He wouldn't mind not always having to come up with all these different (and wonderful) ideas all by Himself. Send your ideas to @Taskmaster, using #TaskmasterBook.

TASK #69

TASK TYPE: Social/Team.

Both teams can compete at the same time.

Special apparatus: everyone needs their phones; mobiles or landlines.

Speak to Simon.

First team to have a conversation with someone called Simon wins.

Your Taskmaster will make sure the person speaking is genuinely a Simon.

Your time starts when your Taskmaster tells you the first three digits of their PIN.

TASK #70

TASK TYPE: Social/Team.

Both teams can compete at the same time.

Special apparatus: two umbrellas.

Repurpose your umbrella.

You have ten minutes.

Most imaginative and successful repurposing of an umbrella wins.

Your time starts when your Taskmaster tells you that it's unlucky to open an umbrella indoors.

CHAPTER 3

Pub Tasks

PUB TASKS

The television show is nearly all filmed in The Taskmaster's now famous lodge, a peculiar purpose-built (presumably) Dutch or something cottage situated somewhere near London's Thames. But every now and again He asks that I take the contestants further afield to accomplish something like scoring a goal with a plastic bag, getting His shopping across a river as quickly as possible or painting a picture of a horse while riding a horse.

So it's now time for you to leave the comfort of your own home and attempt a task or two in other more unusual locations. First up, the setting for long-distance darts and grown-up bedtime storytelling in series 6: the pub (or, if you'd prefer, a restaurant, café, nightclub or hairdresser's).

One of you will again need to be your Taskmaster. If you're really trying to emulate the TV show, that person shouldn't buy any drinks, travel by public transport or go to the toilet unaccompanied.

TASK #71

TASK TYPE: Social.

Everyone can do it at the same time.

At the start of the evening everyone must write down a song title on a piece of paper and hand that piece of paper to your Taskmaster without anyone else seeing it.

Make another contestant sing, hum or whistle your song, without ever overtly asking them.

First person to make another contestant subliminally sing, hum or whistle some of their song wins.

You have until you all say goodbye.

Your time starts when you all say hello.

TASK #72

TASK TYPE: Social.

Everyone can do it at the same time.

Bring back to the table:

One square of toilet paper.

One beermat.

One leaf.

One pen.

One hat.

None of the items may be damaged in any way.

Fastest wins.

Your time starts when your Taskmaster baas.

TASK #73

TASK TYPE: Social.

To be undertaken one at a time.

While ordering, pretend to be from another country.

Most convincing portrayal of the most exotic nationality wins.

Your performance must last at least one minute.

Your time starts when your Taskmaster says, 'Ich bin durstig.'

TASK #74

TASK TYPE: Social.

Everyone can do it at the same time.

Bring back birds.

Everyone, except for your Taskmaster, must leave the table for five minutes and bring back things that are bird related.

Most bird-related things wins.

Your time starts when your Taskmaster squawks.

TASK #75

TASK TYPE: Social.

To be undertaken one at a time.

(A version of this task appeared in series number: 6)

Find something remarkable in common with a stranger.

Once you have persuaded a stranger to take part, each participant must chat to them for three minutes.

Most remarkable things in common wins.

Each person's time starts when your Taskmaster pretends to ring a little bell.

BONUS TASK FACT

The contestants in series 6 were asked to find something in common with my friend Carol. I was hoping they would somehow track down a shared cousin in Milwaukee. Instead, Russell Howard showed her an earwax removal video and Asim Chaudhry boasted about his BAFTA.

TASK #76

TASK TYPE: Social.

To be undertaken one at a time.

Go to the toilets and take a picture of one of your body parts.

Back at the table, give the rest of the group three options as to what body part is in the picture.

The body part guessed incorrectly by the most people wins.

Your time starts when your Taskmaster nearly falls off their chair.

TASK #77

TASK TYPE: Social.

Everyone can do it at the same time.

Everyone must return to the table in five minutes wearing as different an outfit as possible.

You may not swap clothes with a fellow contestant.

Most different outfit wins.

Your time starts when your Taskmaster blurts out, 'All change.'

TASK #78

TASK TYPE: Social.

To be undertaken one by one.

(A version of this task appeared in series number: 2)

Order a drink from the bar without saying the name of the drink you want or any of the following words:

'Please', 'can', 'may', 'I', 'have', 'buy', 'get', 'purchase', 'drink', 'that'.

Also, you may not point at anything or look in the direction of the bartender at any point.

Quickest successful order wins.

Your time starts when your Taskmaster says they need a drink.

TASK #79

TASK TYPE: Social.

Everyone can do it at the same time.

Find someone that looks like you.

The person who finds the person who looks most like them wins.

You have until closing time.

Your time starts when your Taskmaster does a wolf-whistle.

TASK #80

TASK TYPE: Social.

Everyone can do it at the same time.

Everyone must pick a number between one and seven.

Place this book on a flat surface, turn to TASK #124, and walk in the direction of your number.

Furthest distance walked without changing direction within two minutes wins.

Your time starts when your Taskmaster shows you their tan line.

TASK #81

TASK TYPE: Social.

Everyone can do it at the same time.

Have your photo taken with this book and the toughest looking person in the joint.

Toughest person in the book selfie wins.

You have until you're chucked out.

Your time starts when your Taskmaster flexes their brilliant biceps.

TASK #82

TASK TYPE: Social.

Everyone can do it at the same time.

Special apparatus: one beermat each.

Write the best idea on a beermat.

Best new idea wins.

You have three minutes.

Your time starts when your Taskmaster mimes having a lightbulb moment.

TASK #83

TASK TYPE: Social.

Everyone can do it at the same time.

Special apparatus: one coin each.

Place this book in the middle of the table.

**Place a coin in front of each person on the edge
of the table, with some of the coin hanging off
the edge of the table.**

Flick your coin so that it lands and stays on the book.

**Take turns starting with the person with the least hair
and ending with the person with the most hair.**

The person who lands their coin on the book first wins.

**In the event that two or more people succeed in
the same round, these joint winners then take
part in a play-off during which you must all hum
'Greensleeves' as dramatically as possible.**

**The first player starts when your Taskmaster squeals,
'I'm ready.'**

TASK #84

TASK TYPE: Social.

Everyone can do it at the same time.

Special apparatus: one bag of snacks each.

Each person must buy a packet of snacks.

When they have returned with their snacks, they must each fully open their snack packets, social style, so that the packets are entirely flat with the contents in the middle.

Make the best picture of yourself using only your snacks.

Best picture wins.

You have three minutes.

Your time starts when your Taskmaster says they are content that all the packets have been fully opened, social style.

TASK #85

TASK TYPE: Social.

Everyone can do it at the same time.

Special apparatus: as many beermats as you can muster. You can either muster them before the task or make the mustering part of the task. If you can't find enough beermats to all do this task at the same time, take turns at a nearby table and photograph your evidence.

Make the biggest tower using only beermats.

Your tower must stand up completely by itself.

You may only measure your tower when you have balanced a coin – on its edge – on the top of the tower.

You have ten minutes.

Your time starts when your Taskmaster asks someone for the code for the wifi.

TASK #86

TASK TYPE: Social.

Everyone can do it at the same time. This one has multiple winners.
That's nice.

Special apparatus: pens and paper

Without letting your competitors see, write down the name of a pub.

You must not communicate your pub name with anyone else in any way.

You must not write down the name of the pub you are in.

When everyone has written down the name of a pub, reveal your pub names one by one, starting with the person who has visited the fewest countries, and ending with the most travelled person.

Any pair (or more) who have written down the same name wins.

If no one has written the same pub name as anyone else, play again until someone does.

Your time starts when your Taskmaster stretches theatrically.

IMPORTANT: Once you have written down the name of a pub, YOU may not write that name down again in future rounds. Other competitors may, however, write down that name. But if more than two people write down the same pub name, all those people are disqualified.

TASK #87

TASK TYPE: Social.

Everyone can do it at the same time.

Special apparatus: one beermat per person.

Balance a beermat on your head.

When the beermat is balanced you may not touch it again with your hands, or any part of the top half of your body.

First person to convey their beermat from their head to the top surface of one of their feet wins.

If the beermat touches the floor at any point, you must take some refreshment then start again at the top of the task.

Your time starts when your Taskmaster does a convincing sneeze.

TASK #88

TASK TYPE: Social.

Everyone can do it at the same time.

Place three different yellow things in a glass.

Fastest wins.

Your time starts when your Taskmaster sings a bit of the Coldplay song 'Yellow'.

TASK #89

TASK TYPE: Social.

Everyone can do it at the same time.

Swap socks with someone and then swap those socks with someone else.

You may not swap socks with someone from your group.

Fastest wins.

Your time starts when your Taskmaster tells you what colour their socks are.

TASK #90

TASK TYPE: Social.

Everyone can do it at the same time.

Everyone must hold a full drink in the right hand.

Everyone's right arm must be absolutely straight.

Everyone's drink must be no more or fewer than 2cm above the table.

There must be nothing between the drinks and the table at any point.

Whoever keeps their drink at this height the longest without bending their arm wins.

Your time starts when your Taskmaster blows the oldest competitor a kiss.

TASK #91

TASK TYPE: Social.

Everyone can do it at the same time.

Have the best things in your wallet or handbag.

Display three things from your wallet or handbag that prove that you have the best things in your wallet or handbag.

The wallet or handbag containing the best things wins.

You have three minutes to select your best things.

Your time starts when your Taskmaster pretends to be looking at the stars through a telescope.

By now I'm sure you've worked out your way of competing. But just to say that if I was running the evening (quite a large if, realistically), no one would show any of their best things until instructed to do so by your Taskmaster after the three minutes are up.

TASK #92

TASK TYPE: Social.

Everyone can do it at the same time.

> **Your Taskmaster must do an impression of a person using only their face.**
>
> **Guess which person your Taskmaster is representing with their face.**
>
> **If no one has guessed the person after everyone has had three guesses, your Taskmaster can give you one letter of the person's name before each subsequent round, starting with the last letter of the name and working back to their first.**
>
> **Whoever guesses the person first wins.**
>
> **Your time starts when your Taskmaster's impression face is settled.**

TASK #93

TASK TYPE: Social.

Everyone can do it at the same time.

Special apparatus: phones, please.

Show your Taskmaster the coolest picture taken on your phone.

You have a maximum of three minutes.

Coolest picture wins.

Your time starts when your Taskmaster does a really cool gesture.

TASK #94

TASK TYPE: Social.

Everyone can do it at the same time.

(A version of this task appeared in series number: 7)

Special apparatus: everyone must have a pint glass full to the brim.

Each person must tear out one of the strips from the page overleaf and place it on the table.

Fill a pint glass to the very brim with liquid and place it squarely over a strip so that the grey end of the strip is just poking out from under the glass.

Now remove the strip from beneath the pint glass.

You may not move the pint glass and none of the liquid may be spilt.

Fastest wins.

Your time started when the pint was placed on the strip.

BONUS TASK FACT

This is a rare task that actually has a logical solution. If you can't work it out yourself, send the following message to @Taskmaster on Twitter: '#mystripisstuckundermypint #TaskmasterBook' and I'll give you the answer. Not one of Alice Levine, Asim Chaudhry, Liza Tarbuck, Russell Howard and Tim Vine found my recommended technique. They were, however, allowed to move their pints. It's like those celeb versions of quizzes: their questions were easier. Sorry.

TASK #95

TASK TYPE: Social/Team. One member of each team can do this at the same time.

(A version of this task appeared in series number: 6)

One person in each team must write down a list of the most unusual animals.

You must not show or say the names of any of the unusual animals to anyone other than your Taskmaster.

You have two minutes.

Highest number of unusual animals wins.

There is also a bonus point for whichever team writes down the most unusual individual animal.

BONUS TASK FACT

Asim Chaudhry undoubtedly wrote animals that were more unusual than those on Russell Howard's list. Eight-bo*ocked cat, for instance. And laser beam turtle.

---

*||

TASK #96

TASK TYPE: Social/Team.

One team can do this at a time.

(A version of this task appeared in series number: 6)

The person who wrote the list of animals for TASK #95 must communicate the unusual animals on their list to their teammates using only mime.

Most unusual animals successfully guessed wins.

You have five minutes.

Your time starts when your Taskmaster undoes one of their buttons.

BONUS TASK FACT

Unsurprisingly, Russell Howard managed to communicate more of his unusual animals than poor old Asim Chaudhry. Impressively, Asim did manage to convey the generously appointed cat, but that mime ate up nearly all his time.

TASK #97

TASK TYPE: Social/Team.

One team should do this while the others are away from the table. Then that team can watch on while the others have a go. Or, why not buy a second copy of the book and play at the same time?

Put the most things on this book.

Your things must be bigger than grapes.

You have five minutes.

Your time starts when your Taskmaster places the book on the table.

TASK #98

TASK TYPE: Solo.

Sometimes you're in the pub by yourself. That's OK. I'm not judging you. But to make it look like you're not lonely, here's one for you.

Improve the picture of The Taskmaster on the opposite page.

Most improved Taskmaster wins.

You have ten minutes.

Your time starts when you've found a pen.

All of The Taskmaster's houses are covered in pictures of Himself. Of course they are. My own bedroom is similarly decorated so please send me your attempt and I can it add to my enormous collection of pictures of Him.

TASK #99

TASK TYPE: Social.

To be undertaken one by one.

Make the best stain on one of the pages in this book.

Best stain wins.

Each person can have the book for ten minutes.

Your time starts when your Taskmaster hands you the book and tells you to stain it.

'Best' is often a contentious word in *Taskmaster*. You have to guess what your Taskmaster will like. They might be into simulacra – the appearance of religious imagery in natural phenomena – or they might like something that smells funny. Always best to go with your gut instincts, just like The Great Original Actual Taskmaster Himself.

TASK #100

TASK TYPE: Social.

You can take turns doing this task. But bear in mind that when someone accomplishes it, that may well be the end of your task evening. Unless, of course, you did buy two copies of the book, which I would stress is definitely a smart thing to do.

Swap this book for something better than this book.

The thing most better than this book wins.

You have this evening.

Your time has started.

Just like the Prize Task in actual *Taskmaster*, this task provides its own prize. Do let me know if you swap the book for something great, however, and it'll be logged with points duly awarded. Also, if you have received this book in such a swap, please also let me know. I'm pretty keen to track the progress of any book if it's part of a swap chain (although The Taskmaster is also pretty keen that I sort out His hedges so I might not have time).

CHAPTER 4

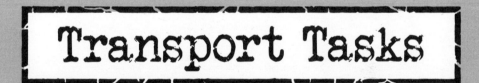

Transport Tasks

TRANSPORT TASKS

As a boy and then as a comedian, I've spent months of my life in a car, staring out of the window. But what could have been a prison sentence (in a car) was actually a walk in the park (in a car) because of games we invented as a family or with fellow stand-ups to pass the time and, more importantly, generate some competition.

A health and safety note here: please don't do anything that could potentially harm yourselves or anyone else. The tasks are important, yes, but not as important as being able to do more tasks in the future.

TASK #101

TASK TYPE: Social.

Everyone can play at the same time in a car.

Spot a red car and shout 'I think I just saw Prince William'.

First person to spot a red car and shout 'I think I just saw Prince William' – without anybody else shouting 'I think I just saw Prince William' during their shouting of 'I think I just saw Prince William' – wins.

Your time starts when there are no red cars in sight.

TASK #102

TASK TYPE: Social.

Everyone can play at the same time in a car.

Say a word that you think will be spoken on the radio.

Your word must contain at least four letters.

The person whose word is spoken first on the radio wins.

You must turn on your radio in two minutes.

TASK #103

TASK TYPE: Social.

Everyone but the driver can play at the same time in a car.

Your Taskmaster will soon turn on the radio.

Any time someone says or sings a word beginning with L you must all look to the right.

Any time someone says or sings a word beginning with R you must all look to the left.

Anyone who makes a mistake or is a bit slow is disqualified.

Last person to make a mistake wins.

Your Taskmaster will turn on the radio when everyone has told them exactly what they think of them.

TASK #104

TASK TYPE: Social.

Everyone can play at the same time in a car.

Have a conversation.

Each person must say between five and ten words, starting with the youngest and working up to the oldest (then starting with the youngest again).

No one may use any words containing any of the letters: 'G', 'R', 'E' and especially 'G'.

There must also not be any unreasonable pauses.

If you break a rule you must leave the conversation.

Last person speaking wins.

The youngest person must start speaking in ten seconds from when everyone understands the rules.

TASK #105

TASK TYPE: Social.

Everyone can play at the same time in a car.

Starting with the person sitting directly behind the driver and going in a clockwise circle from them, sing a musical note for three seconds.

Each person's note must be slightly higher than the previous person's note.

The person who fails to sing a note slightly higher than the previous person's note loses and the group starts again.

The first singer must start low.

Last person singing wins.

The singing starts when your Taskmaster is satisfied with the silence.

'Slightly' is crucial here. Please be hot on 'slightly'.

TASK #106

TASK TYPE: Social.

Almost everyone can play at the same time in a car.

Look out of the window on your side.

Your Taskmaster will count to five.

On 'five' you must all look at each other.

If you are representing the same emotion as someone else with your face you are disqualified.

The representable emotions are:

HAPPY

SAD

ANGRY

MUDDLED

SURPRISED

The task continues until two people remain.

These two must then both clap their hands as many times as possible in one minute.

Whoever claps their hands the most times in one minute wins.

Your Taskmaster will count to five for the first time when they are good and ready.

The driver must not take part in this one either. Sorry, driver.

TASK #107

TASK TYPE: Social.

Everyone can play at the same time in a car.

Predict what colour car the 20th car that passes you will be.

Start counting the cars after the final person has guessed a colour.

The person who gets it right wins and gets to choose the radio station.

You must make all your guesses within ten seconds of your Taskmaster shouting out the name of their favourite teacher.

TASK #108

TASK TYPE: Social.

Everyone but the driver can play at the same time in a car.

Without opening the window or using the car horn, make a pedestrian give you a thumbs up.

Fastest wins.

Your time starts when your Taskmaster sucks their thumb noisily.

TASK #109

TASK TYPE: Social.

Everyone can compete at the same time.

Special apparatus: your Taskmaster needs access to the internet.

Your Taskmaster will say the name of a town or city.

Each person must then say another town or city that they think has a similar population to the town or city said by your Taskmaster.

The person whose town or city has the closest population to that of the town or city said by your Taskmaster wins.

Everyone must say their town or city within 100 seconds of Your Taskmaster saying their town or city.

This task was suggested to me by *Taskmaster* guru (and one of our virtuoso edit producers) Dan Trelfer. He gave me invaluable notes and suggestions for this book so I would love to help spread his 'Population Game' across the population. It began, as most good games do, while he and his friends were eating and drinking in Paris. It has since been played in Utrecht. Do let me know where you adopt the game and if you're able to convince more people to take it with them.

TASK #110

TASK TYPE: Social.

Everyone can play at the same time in a car.

This task is not straightforward but I'm including it because it's a classic Horne family game and I'd love others to play it. Skip ahead if you're alarmed by the amount of words below.

Do not spell out a word.

Starting with the person who has the most money and working towards the person who has the least money, say a letter of the alphabet followed by either 'at the front' or 'at the back'.

Each letter must contribute to an actual word without completing the actual word.

If anyone either completes the word or adds a letter that cannot be part of an actual word, they are eliminated and the others start again.

Other players can challenge if they think someone does not have an actual word in mind when they've said their letter.

Words with three or fewer letters do not count as completed words.

Last remaining player wins.

The task starts when everyone actually understands the rules.

Here's an example. There are five people in a car. The professional footballer starts by saying: 'A.' The lawyer says: 'S at the back.' At this point we have 'AS', which is a word, but it has fewer than three letters so is not a problem. The doctor now says: 'M at the front.' We now have 'MAS' and this is also fine. It's not a completed word but it could still be a word. The teacher says: 'K at the front.' We're on 'KMAS'. It doesn't look like a word or a potential word but the teacher is confident he has an actual word in mind. No one challenges. The young child says: 'T at the back.' We're onto 'KMAST' and everyone is still playing. They know what word they're building. 'E at the back,' says the footballer. 'S at the front,' says the lawyer. 'A at the front,' says the doctor. 'R at the back,' says the teacher. We now have 'ASKMASTER'. The boy is clever. 'S at the back,' he says. 'ASKMASTERS.' The footballer has no choice. 'T at the front,' he reluctantly sighs. He's completed a word and is eliminated and everyone is having fun. Feel free to make it more fun by changing the rules and including words that aren't actual words if the person who has said that word can use it convincingly in a sentence. 'TaskmasterSHIP', for example, as in 'After serving The Taskmaster for six years, the assistant was finally granted a Taskmastership and was allowed to sleep in a bed.'

TASK #111

TASK TYPE: Social.

Everyone can play at the same time in a car.

Make the best word using the letters on the registration plate of the car in front of you.

The letters must stay in the same order as they are on the registration plate, but can be spaced however you like in your word.

Best word wins.

You have one minute.

Your time starts when your Taskmaster firmly says, 'That car.'

Another classic use of 'best'. Your Taskmaster should not necessarily be rewarding the longest word, but the word they deem to be superior to the others.

TASK #112

TASK TYPE: Social.

Everyone can play at the same time in any form of transport in which your Taskmaster can make the necessary calculations.

Special apparatus: a map of where you are (virtual or actual).

Without looking at any sort of technical equipment, guess how far you will travel in the next ten minutes.

The person with the most accurate guess wins and is allowed to sit in the front for the next leg of the journey.

Your Taskmaster will follow the progress of your journey using some sort of clever map system.

You must make your guesses within one minute of your Taskmaster boasting.

TASK #113

TASK TYPE: Social.

Everyone can play at the same time in a car. Someone can play for the driver if the driver trusts that person with their phone.

Special apparatus: your mobile phones.

Every time you pass a motorbike, everyone must count down through their mobile phone contacts to the contact who is the same number contact in their mobile phone as the number on the motorbike's registration plate.

Text that person the following message:

'Wow! I just saw a really cool motorbike!'

Whoever receives the first enthusiastic response wins.

You can start the task when your Taskmaster has read the example on the opposite page in an accent other than their own.

For example, if the motorbike's registration plate is EM15 DUN, everyone must text the 15th person in their contacts; so I would be texting Alan McCarthy (a builder, apparently) and then hoping Alan McCarthy would be really pleased that I spotted a motorbike.

TASK #114

TASK TYPE: Social.

Everyone can play one at a time in a car.

Choose a place to visit based only on a signpost you see on your journey.

You must not have heard of the place before.

Spend 30 minutes in that place.

The person whose place is the best in which to spend 30 minutes wins.

You have your journey.

Your journey started when you all put your straps on.

TASK #115

TASK TYPE: Social.

Everyone but the driver can play at the same time in a car.

While your Taskmaster has their eyes shut, remove an item of clothing.

You have two minutes before your Taskmaster will open their eyes and guess which item of clothing you each removed.

If your Taskmaster correctly guesses which item of clothing you removed you are eliminated.

Continue until there is one winner or no more items of clothing.

Your time starts when your Taskmaster has really tightly shut their eyes.

TASK #116

TASK TYPE: Social.

Everyone can play at the same time in a car.

Special apparatus: mints.

Eat a mint the slowest.

You must all pop your mint in your mouth at the same time.

The mint must remain in your mouth at all times.

Last person with a discernible mint in their mouth wins.

You must pop your mint in your mouth when your Taskmaster snarls, 'Pop your mints in.'

If you'd rather, you may play this with any sort of small confectionery, raspberries or sugar puffs.

TASK #117

TASK TYPE: Social.

Everyone can play at the same time at a service station.

Take a selfie with the most ridiculous thing in the service station.

Most ridiculous service-station selfie wins.

You have five minutes to get your selfie after which you must meet at the massage chairs.

Your time starts when your Taskmaster shouts, 'Do you want to join the AA?'

TASK #118

TASK TYPE: Social.

Everyone can play at the same time at a service station.

Hide something at the service station, then find it again on your return journey.

Anyone who successfully finds their hidden item wins.

Your time starts when you pull into a service station, and ends when you pull out of it again on your final leg.

Obviously, I recommend Tebay or Beaconsfield Services.

TASK #119

TASK TYPE: Social.

Everyone can play one at a time on a plane, coach or train.

Walk the full length of your area of the plane, coach or train, subtly spinning as often as possible.

Whoever completes the most subtle spins on their walk up and down their area wins.

If anyone draws undue attention to themselves, they are disqualified.

Your time starts when your Taskmaster points at you and raises their eyebrows.

TASK #120

TASK TYPE: Social.

Everyone can play at the same time on a plane, coach or train.

Take a picture of the most bald heads on one plane, coach or train.

Most bald heads in one photo wins.

You may not use Photoshop.

You have the length of your journey.

Your time starts as soon as you clock your first dome.

CHAPTER 5

Holiday Tasks

HOLIDAY TASKS

I'm aware that other people go on holidays. If that's you, well done; take these tasks with you and improve your trip.

What He really wants, however, is for you to go on a specific journey, making these tasks your only purpose. And that is how I have been living my life for the last six years.

These tasks can either be undertaken by each member of your travelling group to set up a competitive atmosphere that is so often lacking from normal sojourns, or you may wish to tackle them as one team and then take on the nation's other holiday-makers by sending me your efforts. Either way, good luck and do yourselves and your country proud. Make good choices.

TASK #121

TASK TYPE: Social.

To be undertaken by everyone at the same time.

> ## Travel with the most things that are the same colour.
>
> ## Most things that are the same colour wins.
>
> ## Your time starts when you pack your bags and ends when you unpack your bags at your destination and your Taskmaster inspects what you've brought.

TASK #122

TASK TYPE: Social.

To be undertaken by everyone who is going on a flight at the same time.

Make your bag look the most distinctive on the baggage reclaim conveyor belt.

Most distinctive bag wins.

You have the week before your trip.

Use it wisely.

TASK #123

TASK TYPE: Social.

To be completed individually or as a group on your trip.

Special apparatus: a chair.

Take the best holiday snap with a chair from your home.

The most homely chair in the most un-homely surroundings wins.

You have until your holiday is over.

Your time starts when you reach your destination.

In order to be judged in the nationwide competition for this task, please do send me a picture of your chair in its normal home, as well as its new holiday pose. I need to know you have actually gone to the trouble of bringing (ideally) a (bulky) chair from your house with you on what should be a relaxing experience. Send your pictures to @Taskmaster, using #TaskmasterBook.

TASK #124

TASK TYPE: Social.

To be undertaken by everyone at the same time, wherever you may be.

Special apparatus: a compass (there'll be one on your phone and it's nice you've now got a reason to use it).

Place this book flat on the table, with this page open.

Write down the number of the arrow you think is pointing North.

When everyone has written down a number, check the actual direction of North with a compass.

Nearest wins and becomes the Holiday Taskmaster.

If two or more people write down the same correct number, they must compare tongues.

Longest tongue wins.

The Holiday Taskmaster is in charge. If the person that won the task is not responsible enough to take on that role, feel free to add a time limit of 20 minutes to the title. Not everyone can be a Taskmaster, in the same way that not everyone can be a footballer, the Prime Minister or a really good impressionist.

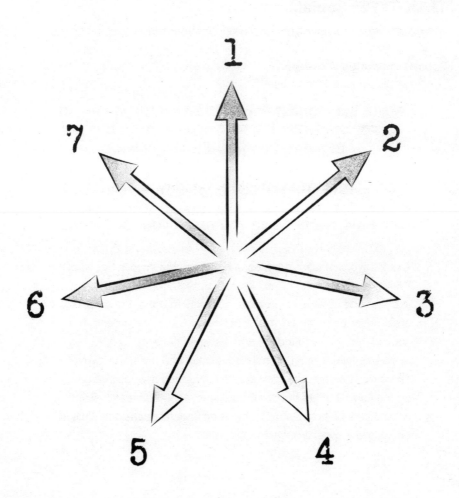

TASK #125

TASK TYPE: Social.

To be completed individually or as a group on your trip.

Special apparatus: a camera.

Make the biggest flag of the country you are in.

Biggest recognisable flag wins.

You have until your holiday is over.

Your time starts when you reach your destination.

A quick word of warning: please be respectful in your flag-making. While asking American *Taskmaster* contestants to make meals in the shape of flags I learnt the hard way that the American flag must never be upside down, must never touch the ground, the floor, water or merchandise, and it should never be carried flat or horizontally. It must be hoisted quickly and lowered slowly. There must be no other flag above it. Nothing may be placed on the flag. The flag must not be displayed in bad weather and should only be brandished at night on special occasions. This is, obviously, a special occasion, but beware.

TASK #126

TASK TYPE: Social.

To be completed individually or as a group on your trip.

Special apparatus: a camera.

Take the worst picture of the best view and the best picture of the worst view.

Worst and best pictures win.

You have until your holiday is over.

Your time starts when you reach your destination.

It takes a certain sort of skill to do something deliberately badly, as you can witness for yourselves if you ever come to see my band The Horne Section in action. I am, by the way, trusting that He won't read this far, otherwise there's no way He'll let me get away with that plug there. Punishments for this sort of thing are not only painful, but I have to set them up so there's also a lot of admin involved.

TASK #127

TASK TYPE: Social.

To be completed individually or as a group on your trip.

Special apparatus: a camera.

Take a photo of yourself holding a postcard so that the postcard blends in with the photo.

Most naturalised postcard wins.

You have until your holiday is over.

Your time starts when you reach your destination.

TASK #128

TASK TYPE: Solo.

To be completed by you while on holiday. Or not on holiday, if you think you live in the best place.

Take a picture of yourself with this book in the best place.

Best place wins.

You have until 31 December 2019.

Your time starts when you've done ten proper squats, really concentrating on your posture.

TASK #129

TASK TYPE: Social.

To be completed individually or as a group on your trip.

Special apparatus: a camera.

Take the best 'tourist propping up the Leaning Tower of Pisa'-type photo.

Best 'tourist propping up the Leaning Tower of Pisa'-type photo wins.

You have until your holiday is over.

Your time starts when you reach your destination.

You know what I mean. By the way, you don't get any extra marks for using the actual Leaning Tower of Pisa but nor will you be docked any if you do.

TASK #130

TASK TYPE: Social.

Everyone can do this at the same time. They must first understand the slightly over-complicated rules though.

> **Guess the total number of fingers that the group is going to show by saying a word.**
>
> **First, everyone must say their word. The number of letters in that word represents the total number of fingers they think the group will show when your Taskmaster counts to five.**
>
> **Second, when your Taskmaster counts to five everyone must show a certain number of fingers.**
>
> **Whoever says a word with the same number of letters as there are fingers on show wins.**
>
> **The game starts when your Taskmaster first counts to five in any language other than English. Or French. Or Spanish.**

TASK #131

TASK TYPE: Social.

To be completed individually or as a group on your trip.

Special apparatus: a camera.

Take a picture of the most best worst use of English you've found on holiday.

Most best worst use of English wins.

You have your entire holiday.

Your time starts as soon as you set foot abroad.

TASK #132

TASK TYPE: Social.

To be completed individually or as a group on your trip.

Special apparatus: a camera.

> **Take a picture of a couple that look most like The Original Taskmaster and His assistant.**
>
> **The couple that look most like The Taskmaster and His assistant win.**
>
> **You have all holiday.**
>
> **Your time starts when you have your first drink.**

TASK #133

TASK TYPE: Social.

To be completed individually or as a group on your trip.

Special apparatus: a camera.

Create the best *Where's Wally?* scene.

Best *Where's Wally?* scene wins.

You have one of your holiday days.

Your time starts as soon as you've had breakfast.

TASK #134

TASK TYPE: Social.

To be completed individually or as a group on your trip.

Special apparatus: something to record your evidence.

Find and demonstrate the most complicated toilet.

Most complicated toilet wins.

You have until your holiday is over.

Your time starts when you set off on your trip.

TASK #135

TASK TYPE: Social.

To be completed individually or as a group on your trip.

Send a postcard to someone using the most negligible address.

Fewest letters on a successfully delivered postcard wins.

You may not use a postcode.

You have as long as it takes.

Your time starts when you purchase your postcard.

CHAPTER 6

Rainy Day Tasks

TASK #136

TASK TYPE: Social.

Everyone can do this at the same time.

Hide the best.

Once hidden, everyone must whisper 'I am here' once every 30 seconds until the task is over.

Last person to be found by your Taskmaster wins.

Your Taskmaster will start searching for you after they have counted to 100 loudly in a voice other than their own.

TASK #137

TASK TYPE: Social.

Contestants must do this one at a time.

Leave the room, give yourself a makeover, then re-enter the room.

Most radical change of appearance wins.

Take it in turns starting with the person who can do the weirdest thing with their body.

Each person has a maximum of five minutes before they must re-enter this room made over.

Your Taskmaster will command each person to leave the room whenever they feel moved to do so.

TASK #138

TASK TYPE: Social.

Everyone can do this at the same time.

Make the longest line of things beginning with the first letter of your first name.

Each of your things must be touching the next thing in your line.

You have five minutes.

Your time starts when your Taskmaster mimes uncorking a wine bottle and drinking the whole thing in one go.

TASK #139

TASK TYPE: Social.

Everyone can do this at the same time.

Special apparatus: plates.

Make the prettiest plate using the rain.

You have five minutes to prepare your plate in whatever way you see fit.

You must then leave your plate outside in the rain for five minutes.

Prettiest plate thanks to the rain wins.

Your time starts when your Taskmaster curls up into a little ball.

TASK #140

TASK TYPE: Social Task

Everyone can do this at the same time.

Gather enough sticks from outside to make the shape on the page opposite TASK #124.

You must gather your sticks within five minutes to qualify.

Wettest person wins.

Your time starts when your Taskmaster rubs their thighs.

Some help with the scoring on this one. To find out who has won, use the following numbers:

Drenched: 5

Sopping: 4

Soaking: 3

Soggy: 2

Damp: 1

CHAPTER 7

Snow or Sand Tasks

TASK #141

TASK TYPE: Social.

To be completed individually or as a group.

Special apparatus: snow or sand. You could also use marshmallows, mashed potato or, if you're Paul Chowdhry, a blue Slush Puppie.

Make the most unusually posed snowman or sandman.

The snowman or sandman with the most standout pose wins.

You have 30 minutes.

Your time starts when you reach the beach or the snow.

So there will be just one winner for this one. No two snowflakes are the same but snowmen often are. Yours can't be. Also, no two tasks are the same, but the next few have some similarities.

TASK #142

TASK TYPE: Social.

To be completed individually or as a group.

Make a modern sand or snow building.

Most fully functioning and ambitious sand or snow building wins.

You have until your holiday is over.

Your time starts when you reach the beach or the snow.

Sand and bouncy are the only areas where castles are still leading the way, architecture-wise. I agree with The Taskmaster that this should no longer be the case. So if you happen to work with bouncy, rather than sand, please do adapt this task to suit your materials.

TASK #143

TASK TYPE: Social.

To be completed individually or as a group.

Build this snowman (or sandman).

The snowman (or sandman) that most resembles the snowman (or sandman) on the page opposite wins.

You have until the next snow melts or the tide comes in.

You'll know when your time has started.

TASK #144

TASK TYPE: Social.

To be completed individually or as a group on your trip to the seaside.

Build this sandcastle.

The sandcastle that most resemble this sandcastle wins.

You have until the tide comes in.

Your time starts when you've got sand between your toes.

TASK #145

TASK TYPE: Social.

To be completed individually or as a group.

(A version of this task appeared in series number: 5)

Special apparatus: a beach or snow and whatever paraphernalia you can find.

Make the best graph on a beach or in the snow.

Best graph wins.

You have until your holiday is over.

Your time starts when you reach the beach or the snow.

BONUS TASK FACT

Bob Mortimer won this task. His graph demonstrated the amount of urine produced per county in the UK. Mark Watson's was about the futility of democracy and Aisling Bea focused on feminism. I think this provides a good hint as to how to impress The Taskmaster.

TASK #146

TASK TYPE: Social.

To be completed as a group.

Spell out the longest word using people lying down on the beach or in the snow.

Longest word or words wins.

You have a whole day.

Your time starts as soon as you persuade someone to lie on the beach or the snow.

TASK #147

TASK TYPE: Social.

To be completed as a group.

Make the most confusing set of footprints in the snow or sand.

Most confusing set of footprints wins.

You have until the snow or sand has been stepped on by too many people.

Your time starts now.

TASK #148

TASK TYPE: Social.

To be completed individually or as a group.

Make the best SnowTaskmaster and SnowTaskmaster's assistant.

Or

Make the best SandTaskmaster and SandTaskmaster's assistant.

You have one hour.

Your time starts when someone in your group screams because the sea/snow is too cold.

TASK #149

TASK TYPE: Social.

To be completed individually or as a group.

**Make the best beach scene in a snowy garden
and the best snow scene on a sunny beach.**

Fastest to complete both scenes wins.

You have until 31 December 2019.

Your time has started.

TASK #150

TASK TYPE: Social.

To be completed individually or as a group, in snow, on the beach, near a forest, in a lake, by a car park or wherever you like.

Take a picture of the weirdest animal.

Weirdest animal wins.

You have one hour.

Your time starts when you next swallow.

CHAPTER 8

Solo Tasks

SOLO TASKS

It's time now for some more tasks that you can tackle by yourself. They're for the serious taskers. They're also for non-serious taskers. Also, you're very welcome to do these solo tasks with other people. It's that sort of book. Like in the show, it's up to you to stretch the rules and words as far as you want.

As I can't be with every one of you, I'm going to have to trust that you will all adhere to the time limits attached to the tasks and not cheat too much, but, apart from that, do what you want. And feel free to cheat. As long as you don't get caught.

If you don't find the attempts themselves fulfilling enough, you can send your results to me on Twitter (@Taskmaster) and I shall award points (5, 4, 3, 2, 1 or 0) and add your efforts to the Global Taskmaster Solo Leaderboard. Whoever is perched atop this league on the very last day of the last year of the second decade of the twenty-first century (31 December 2019) will be richly rewarded. Yes, you could become the Global Taskmaster Champion.

These tasks don't require an awful lot of admin, just maximum effort, imagination and genius. Take them on whenever you feel ready. Go for it. Reach for the stars. Tackle the tasks. Be the best (person who is doing these tasks).

TASK #151

TASK TYPE: Solo or Group.

> **Take a photo with a dog, a cat and a person called Colin in the same frame.**
>
> **Colin must be hiding a flower.**
>
> **Colin must be holding proof that he's called Colin.**
>
> **Fastest photo wins.**
>
> **Your time starts when either of your hands touch something.**

There we go. Get stuck into that. I genuinely can't wait to see your Colins flanked by pets and hiding flowers.

TASK #152

TASK TYPE: Solo.

Read this book in the most extreme situation.

Most extreme situation wins.

You have until 31 December 2019.

Your time started when you began this chapter.

This is a big moment for you. How much do you want this? How extreme will you go? You know that if you want to win you need to go big. But will that please The Taskmaster? As always, it's all up to you. (I would go big. You won't regret it.)

TASK #153

TASK TYPE: Solo.

(A version of this task appeared in series number: 5)

Make this book into the best flick book.

Best flick book wins.

You have until 31 December 2019.

Your time starts when you have flicked something into something.

Enjoy that. It's permission to doodle on our book. Take your time, there's absolutely no need to rush. Make it good.

TASK #154

TASK TYPE: Solo.

**Rip out this page and place it in the copy
of *Taskmaster: 200 Extraordinary Tasks for
Ordinary People* that lives in the British Library.**

Anyone who does this gets five points.

The hundredth person gets a bonus point.

Your time starts when you next smell something.

I have no idea if 100 people will do this. If they do, the 200th
person will also get a bonus point. And so on. If they don't, oh
well, it was a nice idea.

TASK #155

TASK TYPE: Solo or Group.

(A version of this task appeared in series number: 2)

Make the best stop-motion film featuring this book.

Best stop-motion film wins.

You have until 31 December 2019.

Your time starts when you have gathered the necessary equipment.

Don't panic. You don't need an animation studio to make a stop-motion film. Tom, the eldest of my children/task-testers[1], is currently into making his own stop-motion films using Lego, my phone and a free app (there are loads available, have a little Google). It's easy and rewarding. You'll need to take 12 photos for every second of footage. Or 24 if you want to make it look really smooth. Feel free to attempt this many times and send me all of your efforts.

---

[1] The other two, Barney and Dara, would be disappointed if they weren't also name-checked.

TASK #156

TASK TYPE: Solo or Group.

Hit the target on the opposite page in the most impressive way.

Most impressive strike wins.

You have until 31 December 2019.

Your time started when you looked at the target just now.

It's the 'hitting' and the 'impressive' bits that need interpreting from you. I'm expecting great things. I'm also expecting massively disappointing attempts. Don't let me down.

TASK #157

TASK TYPE: Solo or Group.

(A version of this task appeared in series number: 6)

Make the best outfit out of things bought from a stationery shop.

Best stationery outfit wins.

You have until 31 December 2019 and whatever budget you deem appropriate.

Your time starts when you get home from the stationers.

TASK #158

TASK TYPE: Solo.

**Tweet me the answer to this question at exactly
7.19pm and 19 seconds on 1 September 2019
(19.19.19.1.9.19):**

*What is the name of the clock tower on
Chesham High Street opposite JPS Stationers?*

Most punctual correct answers win.

You have until 19.19.19.1.9.19.

Your time is running out.

TASK #159

TASK TYPE: Solo.

Get the best footprint on the page opposite.

Best footprint wins.

You have until 31 December 2019.

Your time starts when you stand up.

Because of the size of the page and the size of some feet, your footprint does not need to be of a full foot. Most of the feet in the world will, however, fit on the page, so do your best.

TASK #160

TASK TYPE: Solo.

Invent a new word.

Your new word must not currently be in the Oxford English Dictionary.

Best evidence of your new word in use wins.

You have until 31 December 2019.

Your time starts when you hear your next word.

TASK #161

TASK TYPE: Solo.

(A version of this task appeared in series number: 4)

Choreograph a dance to a mobile phone ring tone.

Best dance wins.

You have until 31 December 2019.

Your time starts when your phone next rings.

BONUS TASK FACT

Hugh Dennis, Joe Lycett, Lolly Adefope, Mel Giedroyc and Noel Fielding did their dances in front of a green screen. If you have a green screen feel free to use it. If not, I would encourage you to film yourself doing your dance whenever the phone either rings (wherever you may be) or wakes you up. The more elaborate dance in the most unlikely place the better.

TASK #162

TASK TYPE: Solo.

Affix all the labels on the opposite page to the correct things.

The first hundred full sets win ten points.

Your time starts at the next 12 o'clock.

That's a lot of labels, good luck with that one. I'm hoping to receive some full label portfolios before Christmas.

SOUP	RIDICULOUS FROG	OPENING	LAWYER	DOCK LEAF	DOCTOR	DOG	SHAVINGS	TRIPE	BRILLIANT BAGS
BONE	CLASP	20 TEETH	WAXWORK	FIG LEAF	BLUE DRINK	HALF FULL JAR	PONCHO	BRASS	STARFISH
OLD FOOD	HEN	PRETTY BELL	SOMETHING IN AN ICE CUBE	FRANCE	TREAT	CAPE	CLOGS	BRAS	BAIZE
A SILLY BOOK	HENNA	PINE	FAMOUS FOOTBALLER	A HEAP	TREATY	PESTLE	CLAMP	EXCELLENT MAGNET	TAN LINE
SOMETHING SCARY	HENMAN	BRAVE TATTOO	ADRIAN	BROKEN UMBRELLA	GRAVY	MORTAR	CLUMP	PANCAKE	SEAWEED
MEAD	MOUNTAIN	SMILE	ROLLERSKATES	LORRY	TECHNOLOGY	BUNSEN BURNER	FRIEND	AUNT	ROLLER COASTER
A 100 LIRA NOTE	STEAM	CLOAK	HELMET	BLACK CAKE	MOUND	POOL	WINK	FLOSS	BLING
GOLD	AXLE ROD	SWILL	BAD FLAG	CONES	SLIME	LOZENGE	SWAMP	TREASURE	SPECIAL GLOVE
DANCING	MOUSTACHE	TURNIP	NICE PIPE	EXAM	SWORD	MISTAKE	CUE	QUEUE	WET SUIT
WIPES	SICK BAG	MAZE	MONOCLE	GRAZE	BRACES	MILKSHAKE	TOO MANY SOCKS	DIMPLE	SUMMIT

TASK #163

TASK TYPE: Solo.

(A version of this task appeared in series number: 7)

Poke something surprising through the hole you made in TASK #6 of this book.

Most surprising thing wins.

You have until 31 December 2019.

Your time starts on Monday.

TASK #164

TASK TYPE: Solo or Group.

Find a leaf exactly the same size and shape as this leaf.

Most accurate leaf wins.

You have until 31 December 2019.

Your time starts when you go outside.

TASK #165

TASK TYPE: Solo or Group.

Take a picture of yourself drinking the drink
and reading the book written on the nearest
telegraph pole to the task.master.book.

Send your photo to:
Taskmaster's Assistant
PO Box 919
Chesham
HP5 9DH

All correct photos win.

You have until 31st December 2019.

Your time starts when you look up what3words.

TASK #166

TASK TYPE: Solo or Group.

Make the tallest tower of books.

This book must be at the top of the tower and only books may be used to support or build your book tower.

Tallest tower wins.

You have until 31 December 2019.

Your time starts when you close this book.

TASK #167

TASK TYPE: Solo or Group.

Recreate this scene.

Most accurate recreation wins.

You have until 31 December 2019.

Your time starts at 6pm on a Friday night of your choice.

TASK #168

TASK TYPE: Solo or Group.

Write a five-letter word on a postcard and send it to:

Taskmaster's Assistant
PO Box 919
Chesham
HP5 9DH

Anyone who sends the same five-letter word as just one other person wins.

Bonus points will be given to the most thought-provoking postcards.

You may only send one-five letter word yourself.

And you must not tell ANYONE your five-letter word.

I'll have to trust you on all this.

You have until 31 December 2019.

Winners receive a postcard back from me.

TASK #169

TASK TYPE: Solo or Group.

Freeze this page in the most unusual block of ice.

Most unusual block of ice containing this page wins.

You have until 31 December 2019.

Your time starts when you next take off an item of clothing.

TASK #170

TASK TYPE: Solo or Group.

Take photos of yourself beneath as many pub signs as possible in 24 hours.

Most pub signs wins.

Your 24 hours start at noon on the date of your choice.

TASK #171

TASK TYPE: Solo or Group.

Hang the most things off one piece of string.

Neither the piece of string nor anything hanging off it may touch the ground.

The piece of string must only be anchored at either end.

Most things hanging off one piece of string wins.

There is no limit to the length of time or string.

Your time starts when you've found your string and have taken a second to compose yourself.

TASK #172

TASK TYPE: Solo or Group.

Take a picture of a cloud that looks like Hugh Dennis.

The picture of a cloud that looks most like Hugh Dennis wins.

You have until 31 December 2019.

Your time starts when you look at the sky.

BONUS TASK FACT

Good old Hugh. When asked to bring in 'the best membership/subscription' Hugh brought in a subscription to 'Cloud of the Day', a service that sends you a picture of a different cloud every day. He was duly reprimanded for offering up something that a) Greg wasn't into and b) you can see every day in the sky anyway. Secretly, however, I think The Taskmaster loved that man and bought His own 'Cloud of the Day' subscription. I know I like to imagine Lord Greg Davies gazing at some nimbus and letting His worries ebb away.

TASK #173

TASK TYPE: Solo or Group.

Make the best Rube Goldberg machine.

Most complicated machine that completes the simplest task wins.

You have until 31 December 2019.

Your time starts when you've looked up Rube Goldberg machines on YouTube.

Rube Goldberg would have loved *Taskmaster*, I hope. Please do some digging and discover him for yourself. If anyone can come up with a page-turning device for this book to rival his, they'll definitely be on the receiving end of some bonus points.

TASK #174

TASK TYPE: Solo or Group.

Make the kite on the opposite page.

Fly the kite.

Best kite flying wins.

You have until 31 December 2019.

Your time starts when the wind gets up.

TASKMASTER

TASK #175

TASK TYPE: Solo or Group.

Take a picture holding this picture so that your picture lines up exactly in the position in which this picture was taken.

Ideally, I'd be sitting next to a wonderful wine merchant named Sandy.

Most pleasingly accurate picture of the picture held in that position wins.

You have until 31 December 2019.

Your time has started.

TASK #176

TASK TYPE: Solo or Group.

(A version of this task appeared in series number: 1)

Make the best GPS reconstruction of the shape opposite.

The larger and most accurate reconstruction the better.

You have until 31 December 2019.

Your time starts as soon as you have downloaded and mastered a GPS tracker app.

BONUS TASK FACT

Not everyone will understand what any of this means. In short, you can get an app on your phone that tracks your movements and plots them on a map so that you can effectively draw by walking. Frank Skinner, Josh Widdicombe, Roisin Conaty, Romesh Ranganathan and Tim Key attempted this in series 1 with wildly varying degrees of success. Have a look in the Appendix to see their efforts if you need cheering up.

TASK #177

TASK TYPE: Solo or Group.

Make the biggest pattern with the pattern from TASK #124 at the centre of it.

Biggest and best pattern with that pattern at the centre of it wins.

You have until 31 December 2019.

Your time starts when you've worked out how best to take a picture of your big pattern from above.

TASK #178

TASK TYPE: Solo or Group.

Find a four-leaf clover.

Fastest wins.

Your time starts when you leave this room.

TASK #179

TASK TYPE: Solo or Group.

Buy and wear a full monochrome outfit from a charity shop.

The outfit must be made up of at least FIVE different garments, all of which are the same colour.

Best full monochrome outfit wins.

You have until 31 December 2019.

Your time starts when you next look in the mirror.

TASK #180

TASK TYPE: Solo or Group.

Write a message on a stone, place it in a park and get a reply from a stranger.

The quickest and best message from a stranger wins.

Your stone must be no bigger than your palm.

You have until 31 December 2019.

Your time starts when you have written your message on the stone.

As always, it's up to you how you tackle this task. Will the message have your phone number on? That doesn't sound very sensible. Will you be checking your secret stone every hour? Yes, that's much more like it.

TASK #181

TASK TYPE: Solo or Group.

Hang the most mugs off a single tree in the garden.

Most mugs wins.

You have until 31 December 2019.

Your time starts when the kettle's boiled.

TASK #182

TASK TYPE: Solo.

Make the most non-threatening ransom note
using words cut out from this book.

You have until 31 December 2019.

Your time starts when you are happy that this
book is going to have some words cut out of it.

TASK #183

TASK TYPE: Solo.

Rip out the opposite page and hand it to the
person in the picture before he turns 41.

When handing it over you must look him in
the eye, shake his hand and your head and say,
'I think this is your face.'

All successful handovers before his 41st
birthday win.

He's nearly 40 at the time of typing.

Height: 6'2" (little)   Wingspan: 6'2"
Job: Assistant

TASK #184

TASK TYPE: Solo.

(A version of this task appeared in series number: 5)

Make the best book-flinging machine.

Best book-flinging machine wins.

You have until 31 December 2019.

Your time starts when you feel the need to fling this book.

BONUS TASK FACT

Aisling Bea, Bob Mortimer, Mark Watson, Nish Kumar and Sally Phillips were tasked with making coconut-flinging machines. Bea, Kumar and Phillips did their best and their machines were not good. Mortimer and Watson used a crutch and a hat respectively and flung their coconuts a decent distance, simply by placing their coconut in the crutch and the hat and flinging those things. For this task, credit will only be given for machines that are definitely not already things like crutches or hats.

TASK #185

TASK TYPE: Solo or Group.

**Meet on this mound at midday on
14 September 2019.**

(51.706625073 latitude – 0.619552994 longitude)

A Taskmaster Tour begins at 1pm after a picnic.

Bring your own picnic.

TASK #185

TASK TYPE: Solo or Social.

(A version of this task appeared in series number: 7)

Write a 50-word story on the page opposite and
run as far as you can at the same time.

Best story over the furthest distance wins.

You must be running while writing.

You have until 31 December 2019.

Your time starts when you are appropriately
dressed and ready to write.

TASK #186

TASK TYPE: Solo.

Take a picture of the most un-British scene somewhere in Britain.

Most un-British scene wins.

You have until 31 December 2019.

Your time starts the next time you look at your watch.

TASK #187

TASK TYPE: Solo.

Take the four most different photobooth photos in one sitting.

Most varied set of photos wins.

You have until 31 December 2019.

Your time starts when you've saved up the £80 that it costs to use these machines now.

TASK #188

TASK TYPE: Solo.

Take a photo with the most ridiculous number of
knees lined up in a row.

You may not use Photoshop.

The most ridiculous number of knees lined up in
a row wins.

You have until 31 December 2019.

Your time starts when you next hear a bird sing.

TASK #189

TASK TYPE: Solo.

Take a picture of yourself with the most copies of this book.

Your picture must not be taken in or near a bookshop.

You may not use Photoshop.

Most copies of this book in a photo with you wins.

You have until 31 December 2019.

Your time starts when this book next leaves your hands.

TASK #190

TASK TYPE: Solo.

Create your own task.

You have all the time in the world.

All tasks win.

Your time starts now.

If you feel like it, please do send me your tasks. People often do.
I can't guarantee they'll feature in the show but I can guarantee
I'll read them and be tickled by your imagination, and there's not
much better than that. Send your tasks to @Taskmaster, using
#TaskmasterBook.

CHAPTER 9

Advanced Tasks

ADVANCED TASKS

All the tasks, both in this book and in my life, are designed to please The Taskmaster. Of course they are. The Taskmaster is just a great guy, and I want to please great guys.

Sometimes it can be hard to understand why 'spreading your clothes as far and as wide as possible in 20 minutes' or 'removing a table tennis ball from a drainpipe as fast as possible' are so important to The Taskmaster but He has His needs, desires and problems, so who am I, an ordinary guy, to disappoint Him?

Worth bearing in mind, then, that all the following tougher tasks are to be done for Him. When you are struggling to complete what might seem like a pointless and stupid waste of time, remember that it will make Him happy. And although He may (in fact, WILL) never reward you either physically or fiscally, that small smirk that appears once a month on that enormous face of His when something has almost impressed Him should be enough to keep you going.

TASK #191

TASK TYPE: Solo or Group.

**Draw, paint, make or construct the biggest
picture of The Taskmaster.**

Biggest picture of The Taskmaster wins.

You have until 31 December 2019.

Your time starts now.

TASK #192

TASK TYPE: Solo or Group.

Read this book in the most different countries.

Most countries read in wins.

You have until 31 December 2019.

Your time starts now.

I will need proof, of course I will. And that burden lies entirely with you.

TASK #193

TASK TYPE: Solo or Group.

Take a picture of yourself in a queue of people all born in different years, lined up from youngest to oldest.

Most people in a correctly populated queue wins.

You have until 31 December 2019.

Your time starts now.

Bearing in mind that the oldest person in the world, at time of writing, is 116, the maximum score here is 116. Once more, it's up to you to provide evidence supporting your attempt but, to be honest, what I'm looking for is a picture demonstrating human life in all its glory, waiting patiently for something. If you can add an apt detail of what it is they're queuing for you may well get one of The Taskmaster's rare bonus points.

TASK #194

TASK TYPE: Solo or Group.

Paint the biggest thing red.

Biggest thing painted red wins.

Remember the rule about not breaking the law.

You have until 31 December 2019.

Your time starts now.

TASK #195

TASK TYPE: Solo or Group.

Recycle this book.

Most worthy recycling of this book wins.

You have until Earth Day 2019.

Your time started when you bought this book.

TASK #196

TASK TYPE: Solo or Group.

To be undertaken only by people over the age of 18 who haven't drunk alcohol that day and who are completely sure this is what they want to do with their bodies.

Get a *Taskmaster*-related tattoo.

Best *Taskmaster*-related tattoo wins.

Your time started when Josh Widdicombe set the ball rolling in series 1 by getting a tattoo of the word GREG on his foot.

TASK #197

TASK TYPE: Solo or Group.

(A version of this task appeared in series number: 1. The Swede appeared in series 1, 2, 3 and 4 but then the Swede went back to Sweden.)

Make a Swedish person blush.

You will receive extra points if your Swedish person is Fred, our Swedish person.

Best blushing Swede wins.

You have until 31 December 2019.

Din tid börjar nu.

TASK #198

TASK TYPE: Solo or Group.

Send The Taskmaster's assistant something unusual.

The most unusual thing that reaches: Taskmaster's Assistant, PO Box 919, Chesham, HP5 9DH wins.

You have until 31 December 2019.

Your time is precious.

BONUS TASK FACT

James Acaster, Jessica Knappett, Kerry Godliman, Phil Wang and Rhod Gilbert were all set this task in the course of the latest series but only Mr Wang completed it. The other four simply didn't. Unfortunately for Phil, this resulted not in an extra five points pinging into his Taskmaster account, but the whole task being dropped and his purchase of a boomerang in Australia and its subsequent postage from New Zealand to Chesham futile. His package did have such a good name, however, that I feel obliged to at least include it here so someone somewhere might still get to appreciate the efforts of a man who sent me my first 'BoomerWang'.

TASK #199

TASK TYPE: Solo or Group.

Destroy this book as beautifully as possible.

Most beautiful destruction wins.

You have until 31 December 2019.

Your time started when you opened this book.

TASK #200

TASK TYPE: Solo or Group.

Get the best ten autographs on the page opposite.

A-listers get five points.

B-listers get two points.

Anyone else I've heard of gets one point.

Any previous *Taskmaster* contestant gets ten points.

Best ten autographs wins.

You have until 31 December 2019.

Your time starts when you next see any sort of screen.

CHAPTER 10

Surprise Tasks

SURPRISE TASKS

By now *Taskmaster* contestants should really expect that not all is what it seems. There have been twists and turns since the first series: secret tasks, mischievous traps and hidden messages. But no, ever since Josh Widdicombe was the only contestant asked to count all the baked beans in a can of beaked beans, every quintet has failed to find our Easter Eggs. See the Appendix for a full rundown of *Taskmaster* tricks.

So these final few tasks are a bonus for you. They're not part of the 200 mentioned on the cover, they're not in the contents; they're an extra, just for you.

TASK #201

TASK TYPE: Solo.

Complete the task hidden in this book.

Here is your clue:

Take the sixth letter of my name and an extraordinary photo, chat to a stranger then improve the Taskmaster before walking in a direction of your choice and casting a special shadow.

Fastest wins.

Your time started when the first person bought this book.

TASK #202

TASK TYPE: Solo.

Find the mistakes in this book.

Most mistaskes found wins.

You have until 31 December 2019.

Your time starts when you next drop something.

TASK #203 (THE ULTIMATE TASK)

TASK TYPE: Solo.

Complete every task in this book in 203 days.

Fastest wins.

Your time started when you bought this book.

APPENDIX

ART

Apart from the cast and all the tasks and Greg's facial hair and eyewear, not a lot changes in the *Taskmaster* world from series to series. I spend more time at that house than my own so it's a familiar and safe place for us to do stupid things.

But like any happy household, we constantly make small unnecessary improvements and subtle changes that I hope even one viewer notices. Every series, for instance, has a themed artist (as all proper comedy shows should). Here are those artists, and my favourite fact about each one:

Series 1 – Andy Warhol: his birthday was never recorded so he changed the date most years.

Series 2 – Salvador Dalí: he loved cauliflowers so much he once arrived at a lecture in Paris in a Rolls-Royce filled to the brim with the vegetable.

Series 3 – Roy Lichtenstein: his 1962 pop art painting *Masterpiece* sold in January 2017 for $165 million. That's a lot of money for a single one liner.

Series 4 – Vincent van Gogh: he didn't paint his first painting until his tkday (a milestone that marks your 10,000th day, which occurs during your 28th year on Earth).

Series 5 – René Magritte: he wanted to have an affair with an artist called Sheila so asked his friend Paul to distract his wife Georgette. This backfired when Georgette started her own affair with Paul.

Series 6 – M.C. Escher: he nearly designed the banknotes for the Dutch Central Bank (but his ideas were ultimately rejected for being 'too ornate').

Series 7 – Pablo Picasso: his full name is Pablo Diego José Francisco de Paula Juan Nepomuceno María de los Remedios Cipriano de la Santísima Trinidad Martyr Patricio Clito Ruiz y Picasso.

CLUES

A favourite team task featured in series 6, in which Russell Howard and Alice Levine faced off against Asim Chaudhry, Liza Tarbuck and Tim Vine, was the following:

Find the link, then do it exactly 100 times.

Fastest wins.

Your time starts now.

Feel free to try to solve it yourself. Below is a full list of the clues the contestants were given. The answers and overall link is in the footnote, so try to resist looking there for now.

A toy bunny rabbit nestled in what looked and smelt like a litter tray.

A hotel bell.

A bottle of Scotch.

A shopping list with letters circled that spelled out 'Guy from Steps'.

Damien Rice's debut.

The word 'urinating'.

A map of Europe with some short flights highlighted; Luton to Belfast, Stansted to Edinburgh, that sort of thing.

The word 'hopelesslesseless'

Lyrics to the popular song 'Jump Around'.

A picture of an overhead projector with a recycle symbol next to it.

The words 'Arnold J. Rimmer'.

The words 'No J. Simpson'.

The words 'Diddy's first'.

The words 'Patrick Bateman – Hannibal Lecter – in the middle of these two.'

A lock with the combination 8-15-16[1].

FAILURES

When you feel ready to tackle TASK #190 (Create your own task), please don't come up with any of the following. These are a few of the tasks we have tried, sometimes on several occasions, but which did not make their way into the show. Hopefully the reasons given will provide some guidance as to what makes a good task, and what makes the production team and the comedians waste their valuable time and get cross with you on five consecutive days:

Skim a biscuit.

---

[1] Bunnies hop. The litter tray was filled with odorous hops. Hotels have bellhops. Hopscotch. H. O. Pee. Short-hop flights. Hopeless less eless = hop. House Of Pain. OHP = HOP. Rimmer has 'H' on his forehead for 'Hologram'; Simpson's first initial is 'O'; Diddy's is 'P': H. O. P. (Also, it was pointed out to me on Twitter that Arnold J. Rimmer's parents were Seventh Day Advent Hoppists. That's the sort of viewers we have and I love.) They are both psychopaths: in the middle of psycHOPaths is HOP. The 8th, 15th and 16th letters of the alphabet are H, O and P. Also, there was some red string tied on the wall behind the clues that spelt out H O P if you stepped back and squinted. The link, as I hope you've guessed by now, is HOP.

Most biscuit bounces wins.

You may have three attempts with one style of biscuit.

We tried this in series 2. We offered our contestants five different types of biscuit, including Bourbon and Jammy Dodger. It turns out it is too difficult to tell when a biscuit skim becomes a biscuit float. Feel free to show me evidence to the contrary, as long as you promise to use fish-friendly biscuits (no pink wafers).

Burst all the bubbles in this roll of bubble wrap.

Fastest wins.

Your time starts when you burst your first bubble.

We tried this task with the contestants of series 1 and series 3. The roll of bubble wrap was 5 metres long. That's a lot of bubbles. I know, because I (among others) had to count them. We were hoping that by starting the timer when they burst their first bubble, our inventive comics would think of a method that wouldn't simply involve them bursting all those bubbles individually.

Some promising plans were made. Tim Key found a large garden roller, Paul Chowdhry borrowed my van, Josh Widdicombe kneeled down next to the bubble wrap and wielded a knife. Unfortunately, bubble wrap is a brilliant invention. It is designed not to be popped quickly. Both van and roller simply squeezed the air around the roll and failed to pop the bubbles. Josh is not particularly quick with a knife. All contestants ended up at some point jumping on the bubbles, and finally wringing them out one by one. None took less than 20 minutes and all attempts were deemed too dull to be shown on TV.

In Sweden, however, where 'health and safety' and 'worrying about the environment' are apparently not phrases anyone says with a straight face, one contestant doused the roll with petrol, chucked on a match and swung it round his head, littering the garden with flames but bursting the bubbles in an instant. I do not recommend you try that at home but I do appreciate it's probably the fastest method.

Get the most signatures while dressed as a parrot.

You have 30 minutes.

Your time starts now.

For this ultimately pointless task we made all the series 1 contestants don an enormous parrot costume in a meeting room somewhere deep in High Wycombe's Eden shopping centre, before guiding them to a spot just outside a jewellery shop where they were to persuade passers-by to sign a piece of paper. The costume was full, heavy and unfeasibly hot. Nobody knew that Frank Skinner was sweating inside the parrot or that Romesh Ranganathan was the man in the bird shouting at children.

Unbelievably, perhaps, this was the one task in which we felt the comedians had to lose their dignity (as opposed to the many in which they themselves chose to shed it), and so the task was consigned to the cutting-room floor. It was more of a prank than a task.

If you happen to be one of those people who signed a piece of paper in a mall in the spring of 2015 because a massive angry bird told you to, this will finally explain why you didn't then receive the free parrot gift pack you were promised.

Represent the planets using fruit.

Most accurate size and order of planets wins.

You have three minutes including, if you wish, one phone call lasting no longer than one minute.

This still looks like a good task to me. But the trouble with the contestants of series 4 was that they all actually knew their planets well enough to represent them accurately with fruit. A task never works if everyone succeeds[2]. By actually being good at something, Hugh Dennis, Joe Lycett, Lolly Adefope, Mel Giedroyc and Noel Fielding managed to make this seem more like a demonstration for a kids' TV show than a challenging test of wit and skill on Dave.

Just so you know, Hugh called the BBC's head of radio comedy, Joe phoned his mate Ben who had excellent wifi, Lolly and Mel called their brother and mum respectively while Noel tried and failed to get through to Professor Brian Cox.

---

[2] The exception being the removal of a tablecloth from under eggs in series 6.

GIFT IDEAS

It's getting harder to think of what to get him, isn't it? You've already bought him a personalised picture, some special socks and a box of beers from around the world. No one listens to CDs or watches DVDs any more. And yes, he's already got the only book/boardgame/programme-companion *Taskmaster – 200 Extraordinary Tasks for Ordinary People* that anyone could ever need.

Well, thankfully for you, the first 15 contestants on *Taskmaster* were all given one task that remains the only one to be repeated across series:

Buy the best gift for The Taskmaster.

You have 12 weeks.

Your time starts now.

Within the task there was also a £20 note. It didn't say anything about whether or not the comics (and Richard Osman) had to stick to this amount but they mostly did, meaning that all the following may well prove to be both thoughtful and affordable presents for your own loved ones.

See if you can match the items to the donors (answers in the footnotes below[3]):

1. Bespoke comic portrait of Greg
2. Betting slip for a horse race worth £20 (the horse won and the money went to charity)
3. Book tokens worth £16 and a card worth £4
4. A cookbook of recipes from films and 701 penny sweets
5. Footstool to match The Taskmaster's throne
6. Last Rolos worth £20
7. Lordship title
8. Memorabilia from the town Wem (Wemorabilia): The Story of Wem, a programme from Wem Town FC, a bottle from the Wem and Salop brewery, 'Wem', a single by German-South African singer-songwriter Howard Carpendale
9. Pair of 'spy' aviator sunglasses (with built-in mirrors to allow you to see the person behind you)
10. Pair of water skis
11. Script for a future episode of *Man Down*
12. Secondhand baseball bat and helmet
13. Tattoo of the word Greg on a foot
14. Three lottery scratch cards and a mouse
15. Twister, the game

---

[3] 1. Romesh Ranganathan, 2. Richard Osman, 3. Tim Key, 4. Jon Richardson, 5. Rob Beckett, 6. Al Murray, 7. Katherine Ryan, 8. Dave Gorman, 9. Frank Skinner, 10. Joe Wilkinson, 11. Sara Pascoe, 12. Doc Brown, 13. Josh Widdicombe, 14. Roisin Conaty, 15. Paul Chowdhry.

GPS

If you enjoyed TASK #176 (making the best GPS reconstruction of my face), here are five more shapes you can attempt to reconstruct on foot.

JOIN THE DOTS

Please do bear in mind that Alice Levine, Asim Chaudhry, Liza Tarbuck, Russell Howard and Tim Vine were wearing high heels when making the dot-to-dot pictures below. See if you can work out what they were meant to be and feel free to interpret/improve them. Actual answers in the footnote below[4].

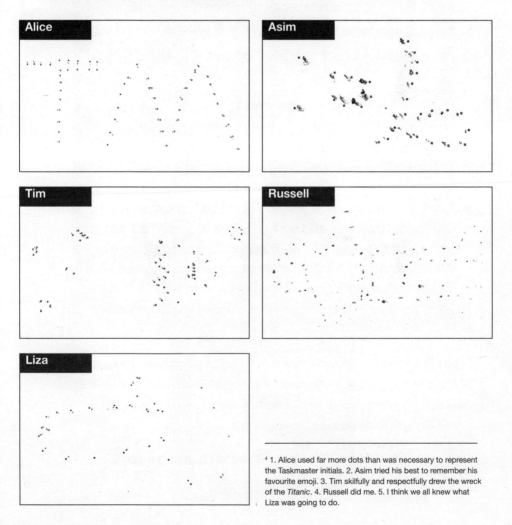

Alice

Asim

Tim

Russell

Liza

[4] 1. Alice used far more dots than was necessary to represent the Taskmaster initials. 2. Asim tried his best to remember his favourite emoji. 3. Tim skilfully and respectfully drew the wreck of the *Titanic*. 4. Russell did me. 5. I think we all knew what Liza was going to do.

MATHS

If you've ever wondered how many beans there are in a can of baked beans, you don't need to pour them out and count them, because Josh Widdicombe has already done that for you. So here, thanks to Mr Widdico M.B.E., are the numbers you may one day need to know:

Number of baked beans in a can of baked beans: 406
Number of spaghetti hoops in a can of spaghetti hoops: 433
Number of grains of rice in a 500g packet of rice: 25,000

POETRY

The question I am asked most often is 'What is your favourite task?' (closely followed by, 'Wow, so how tall is Greg?' and 'What time is it?'). As mentioned in TASK #49, the answer I usually give is one from the second series, in which the contestants were taken to Chesham Town Hall and walked into a room to find that year's mayor, a suitably magnificent-looking man called Councillor Peter Hudson. In front of him lay the envelope, its red wax seal looking more apt than ever. 'Impress this mayor' read the contestants. 'Are you a real mayor?' they all asked. Cllr Peter Hudson nodded and smiled. 'You have 20 minutes. Your time starts now.'

I love this task for several reasons. I live in Chesham and am proud of the town. Making the likes of Katherine Ryan and Joe Wilkinson aggressively twerk and run to Sainsbury's is even more fun when your children's teachers are watching.

So here are Katherine Ryan and Richard Osman's eulogies to the world's finest town:

Richard Osman (reciting from memory while juggling):

One fine day to Chesham fair
I ventured forth to meet the Mayor.
Strong of jaw and fine of feature,
The King of Chesham, my new friend Peter.
Peter's on our list of crushes
In this town of boots and town of brushes.
Foes he has many, but he'll just kick 'em
From Aylesbury, Chartridge and High Wycombe.
Of Amersham we don't give two 6-21-3-11-s.
Chesham: third biggest town in Bucks.

Katherine Ryan (singing and twerking and wearing hip-hop trousers):

Listen up kids,
We're going to bin the Lord's Prayer
Big ups to the big guy,
That's Chesham's Town Mayor.

That's Peter Hudson.
You know that you can trust him. Yeah.

Is he sexy? Affirmative.
Brown hair, brown eyes, Conservative.
A volunteer, but that's not all.
Three kids but just one came from his balls.

That's Peter Hudson.

You know that you can trust him. Yeah.

Recreation and the arts.
His general interests: food and darts.
Organises Dial-a-Ride;
A politician with nothing to hide.

That's Peter Hudson.
You know that you can trust him. Yeah.
That's Peter Hudson (everybody)
You know that you can trust him. Yeah.
That's Peter Hudson.
You know that you can trust him.

And, as promised, here is a poem made out of the five-letter words offered up for TASK #2, the very first to be undertaken by the inaugural five Taskmaster competitors. Not all of the words are five letters long because not all of the competitors were good at the tasks.

Alan Sugar, Jesus Christ
Tiger Woods, really moist
Oh my God, Naked Monks
Holy Cow, Extra Funks

Quick slick solid moles
Fast lying natty voles
Honey cheese bread dream
Toast spuds gravy cream

David Bowie, Queen, Doves

Tears for fears, Cream, Suggs

Alan Sugar needs Jeans

David Bowie bites beans

Friends, Drinks, Fries, Chips

Spoon Forks Spoon Knife

Table, Chair, Shoes, Feets

Longest five minutes of my life.

RECIPES

If you have a spare ten minutes and are hungry, here are five different ways of making Marmite (thanks to Stevie Saponja for compiling):

Aisling Bea's Marmite

Ingredients:

Tomatoes; tinned, normal
 sized, cherry & sundried
 (in a jar)
Marmite
Balsamic vinegar
Onions
Salt & pepper
Miso paste
Bread (wholegrain, sliced)
Round label stickers
Colouring-in pens
Mustard
Miso paste
Beans – cannellini
Non-specific brand brown sauce
Olive oil

Method:
(Preparation time: 10 minutes)

1. Taste actual Marmite.
2. Chop then fry onions in oil.
3. Add bean juice to give that 'sandy, crappy taste'. Then add tinned tomatoes and some beans.
4. Leave to stew, add brown sauce, balsamic vinegar and some chopped tomatoes.
5. Add a pile of miso paste for that 'crappy taste that isn't right'.
6. Blend mixture then pour into Marmite-jar-shaped jar.
7. Spend remaining time designing label.

Bob Mortimer's Marmite:

Ingredients:

24 beef stock cubes
2 tins of treacle
Salt
Sugar
Bovril
Stevia syrup (sugar substitute)
Black food colouring

Method:
(Preparation time: 10 minutes)

1. Mix 5 beef blocks into 1 tin of treacle.
2. Stir semi-professionally.
3. Add more beef blocks to taste (approx. 14).
4. Add a generous dash of Bovril for darkness.
5. Mix in a further 3 beef cubes.
6. Add black food colouring then decant into Marmite-jar-shaped jar.

Sally Phillips's Marmite(s)

Ingredients:

Celery salt
Sherry
Absinthe
Chilli
Baking glitter
Small toy car
Stickers
3 more jars
Brown sauce
Powdered onion
Brown sugar
Powdered yeast
Cornflour
Molasses
Red food colouring
Pot of Nutella
Air-dry clay
Small trophy
Super glue
Labels
Small musical instruments
   (a kazoo and a horn)

Method:
(Preparation time: 10 minutes)

1. Pour absinthe into one jar and seal.
2. Spoon Nutella into one jar, add glitter, seal then shake to mix. Affix stickers to the jar before gluing a small trophy to the top and resting a kazoo inside the trophy.
3. Put a toy car into one jar, seal and label as 'Best Marmite'.
4. Mix sherry, remaining absinthe, cornflour, yeast, red food colouring & brown sauce.
5. Decant the mixture into the fourth jar, seal and finish with a small air-dry clay sculpture on top.

Kumarmite:

Ingredients:

A gentleman's tin (jar) of
   Marmite x2
Sliced white, and slice brown
   bread
A small bottle of champagne
Salt
Yeast extractor (syringe)
Dark chocolate
Brown sugar
Vinegar

Method:
(Preparation time: 10 minutes)

1. Extract the yeast from the bread with the yeast extractor (syringe).
2. Mash up some bread.
3. Add some brown sugar.
4. Soak the bread in vinegar.
5. Add some dark chocolate and let it rest in there.
   (Put some Marmite in the jar for plan b.)
6. Add a kettle full of boiling water to the mixture.
7. Spoon the mixture into the Marmite-jar-shaped jar.

Mark Watson's Marmite:

Ingredients:

10 beef stock cubes
Brown (wholemeal) flour
The darkest lard possible
Dark food colouring
Bovril in a jar
Dark jam (blackcurrant)
Dark dates
Dark prunes
Fairly dark butter

Method:
(Preparation time: 10 minutes)

1. Mix 3 stock cubes into half a mug of boiling water.
2. Add most of a jar of Bovril.
3. Add brown flour to thicken the mixture.
4. Pour in food colouring to drown out lumpiness.
5. Add a bit of lard to gloopify and make the texture interesting.
6. Drown out lard with pestle and add one more stock cube.
7. Add a generous dash of balsamic vinegar, add more flour to drown out lard residue.
8. Pour Marmite into Marmite-jar-shaped jar.

STATISTICS

Here is a full break down of who did how well in the first six series, combined with the US series. It was voluntarily compiled by Alex McMillan who explained to me that his girlfriend, Laura, and he are fans of the show and 'the spreadsheet was more to allow the two of us to immediately settle any disputes over who is better than who (we both had a feeling Katherine Ryan was definitely the best contestant at the time, but wanted to have some numbers to back it up). Up until last month I was working on a Master's dissertation which involved filtering and analysing data from 150 races in *Mario Kart 64*, so I had the Excel sheet pretty much ready to adapt.'

That's all very well but the main message here is that this sort of unwarranted compilation of information definitely means that Taskmaster should absolutely be considered a sport and appear at all future Olympics.

(Point Per Rabbit Converted)	Total Score	Tasks played	Episodes played	Episodes Won	Average score per task	Avg score per episode	Series Final Ranking
Rob Beckett	123	38	7	2	3.24	17.57	1st
Noel Fielding	176	55	10	1	3.20	17.60	1st
Jon Richardson	88	28	5	1	3.14	17.60	2nd
Josh Widdicombe	132	42	8	3	3.14	16.50	1st
Katherine Ryan	119	38	7	2	3.13	17.00	1st
Kate Berlant	75	24	4	4	3.13	18.75	1st
Liza Tarbuck	181	58	10	2	3.12	18.10	1st
Bob Mortimer	161	53	10	3	3.04	16.10	1st
Mark Watson	130	43	8	2	3.02	16.25	2nd (Joint)

Sally Phillips	130	43	8	3	3.02	16.25	2nd (Joint)
Tim Vine	175	58	10	2	3.02	17.50	2nd
Joe Lycett	135	45	8	2	3.00	16.88	2nd
Mel Giedroyc	134	45	8	3	2.98	16.75	3rd
Aisling Bea	127	43	8	0	2.95	15.88	4th
Russell Howard	170	58	10	3	2.93	17.00	3rd
Richard Osman	82	28	5	2	2.93	16.40	3rd
Frank Skinner	93	32	6	2	2.91	15.50	2nd (Joint)
Romesh Ranganathan	93	32	6	0	2.91	15.50	2nd (Joint)
Dave Gorman	81	28	5	1	2.89	16.20	2nd
Freddie Highmore	69	24	4	1	2.88	17.25	2nd (Joint)
Ron Funches	69	24	4	0	2.88	17.25	2nd (Joint)
Hugh Dennis	129	45	8	1	2.87	16.13	4th
Al Murray	80	28	5	1	2.86	16.00	3rd
Lolly Adefope	125	45	8	1	2.78	15.63	5th
Tim Key	88	32	6	1	2.75	14.67	4th
Asim Chaudhry	159	58	10	1	2.74	15.90	4th
Lisa Lampanelli	63	24	4	2	2.63	15.75	4th
Alice Levine	152	58	10	2	2.62	15.20	5th
Sara Pascoe	72	28	5	0	2.57	14.40	4th
Dillon Francis	61	24	4	1	2.54	15.25	5th
Doc Brown	70	28	5	1	2.50	14.00	4th
Nish Kumar	107	43	8	0	2.49	13.38	5th
Paul Chowdhry	66	28	5	1	2.36	13.20	5th
Joe Wilkinson	61	28	5	0	2.18	12.20	5th
Roisin Conaty	68	32	6	1	2.13	11.33	5th

STORIES

Series 7 sees James Acaster, Jessica Knappett, Kerry Godliman, Phil Wang and Rhod Gilbert attempting to write by hand a ten-word story while running 50 metres in the fastest time. It's a good task. But back in series 4 we asked Hugh Dennis, Joe Lycett, Lolly Adefope, Mel Giedroyc and Noel Fielding to run twice that distance, the full length of the Meadow (home, of course, of the mighty Chesham United), with a surprisingly heavy old-fashioned typewriter strapped to their chests, with the instruction to type a 50-word story while sprinting in the middle of a fiercely cold winter. The task did not make it to air as it looked more like torture than tasking and the typewriters refused to work properly because of the sub-zero temperatures, but here is Lolly's moving effort.

Once upon a time there was a girl called Lolly and she was twenty five years old. She was single and ready to mingle. She met her soulmate in a bar. He was a librarian and he always wore black. He was extremely clean. They lived happily together for the rest of their short lives.

Words: 55 words

Time: 4 minutes 3 seconds

TEXTS

Here are a fifth of the cheeky texts sent by Mark Watson to The Taskmaster over a six-month period, which gained him a total of zero points because there was a single day on which he failed to send one.

Hey sexy! Just getting in touch. This is the first of 150 messages. You're in for a treat!!

Hey Taskie. Don't worry about not replying yesterday. We've got so much time ahead of us

Just having a curry. I can think of some ways you could make it spicier!

My birthday today. It would feel like my birthday every day if you were here. I'm in Leicester. You? Cheeky half!?

I'm in London. You? Cheeky half?

Off to see Moonlight. It won the Oscar. Should be in for a treat. Would be more of a treat if …

It was good - maybe not as good as Man Down.

Or Cuckoo

Couple of wines down. I love you man. I don't mind that you don't reply. I know what we have.

I'm just in my undies.

Do the others do this for you? Like I do?

Wearing some new jeans that you would like.

Wearing nothing at all

Can you lend me fifty quid? Different sort of cheeky, this.

Fifty quid just to get some stuff like petrol

Naked except for my socks.

Any update on that cash gift? At a stretch I can take a cheque if you don't have notes.

I hope I didn't embarrass you with all that talk about trying to borrow money …

… I just felt like we'd had enough 'cheeky texts' to get to know each other, and now it's time to open up a bit.

And obviously, you've done pretty well for yourself

So I'm going to stop beating about the bush asking for £50 or £100 here or there.

And I'm going to come straight to the point: can I have thirty grand?

Thirty grand, thirty thousand pounds. I know you've got a fair bit put by, and it would make the world of difference.

I can't wait till July, to finally be able to see you and catch up with you in person.

Mate - this is really awkward - the ££ isn't in my account yet?

Sometimes (I'm only saying this to clear the air) you can be a bit distant.

Like, to give one example, I've been texting you since February 9th without hearing back.

I know I said I didn't mind. Back when this started. But, I don't know, anyone would feel weird sending 100 texts and not hearing back.

Is there any chance I could have some extra points? Again I hate asking.

But I really messed up some of the tasks you see.

TRICKS

The *Taskmaster* audience is special, in every conceivable way. After seven series and fuelled initially by Josh's bean counting, they suspect tricks that we hope no one will notice, spot threads that we didn't mean to include and absolutely love an Easter Egg. The contestants, however, are rarely so wary.

Jon Richardson was the unwitting solo recipient of four bonus tasks in series 2. Each of his rivals was given the task of inventing their own brand new two-minute task. These were then given to Jon who, after regaining his composure, had to guess who had set which tasks. He got all four right, won some bonus points and nearly forgave us.

In series 3, the contestants were asked to pop a lot of balloons as fast as possible. The balloons were a combination of long and round shapes arranged in different colours across a couple of lines. Al Murray was the only one who saw that they resembled Morse code but even he didn't translate the secret message so missed an easy win.

A couple of episodes later, Paul Chowdhry was the only one given the opportunity to 'have the most fun on this bouncy castle'. That cost the production an hour and a fair amount of honk, but the joyful films it produced were priceless.

As mentioned in TASK #24, while sweating as much as possible, Rob Beckett was also told to speak in as many different accents as possible. He did his best and we all very much enjoyed it.

Mel Giedroyc created her own mystery in series 4 by collecting every wax seal from every task and placing them in her jumpsuit pocket. Countless people have asked me what she did with them. I know, of course, but unfortunately I am not at liberty to tell you or anyone else unless I'm with Mel at the time, which I'm not.

The Taskmaster did instruct me to try to rile the unflappable Giedroyc by asking her alone to inflate an 8-foot diameter beach ball in a small room, then score a goal with it outside (meaning it had to be deflated to get it outside), then hide it on the Chesham United football pitch (impossible). She was briefly irked, as was Noel Fielding when I got him to spray a graffiti representation of me 'looking cool' on my garden shed. It didn't feature in the show but still makes me smile every day.

Smiling is what it's all about. Just ask Joe Lycett. During the long-distance painting task in series 4, Joe alone was asked to smile with increasing enthusiasm every 30 seconds during his attempt. He did so with pure professionalism.

Credit to Lolly Adefope in that series too, who was the only one of the five who had to shepherd three chickens onto a small red carpet circle. The plan was for them all to attempt this really quite fiddly feat, but an outbreak of avian flu shortly after her attempt meant that the birds had to be kept indoors and we had to replace them with dogs for the other four.

In series 5, I tasked myself with secretly saying a pun featuring fish (or the odd aquatic mammal) every time Sally Phillips stepped up. This was actually more taxing and embarrassing for me than Sally but did culminate in her own special moment, as she waded way out into Frensham Pond where she was asked to make as many fishy puns as possible in 60 seconds. Because I managed to say far more over four months, without her ever noticing, than she did in that one minute I was awarded my first and only ever Taskmaster point.

Sally's fish puns (made under pressure in one minute wearing waders in the middle of a pond):

Stop carping on.
Cod do this. (That was her pun on 'can't do this'.)
Can you make lots of fish puns? I trout it. I trout it very much.
I've got my herring a bun.
I can sing a rainbow trout.
He's not very tuna-ful.
Minnow understand English.

Send in the clownfish.

Alex's fish puns (made over the course of eight months whenever in Sally's presence):

I don't want to carp on about it.
It doesn't say you can't ask salmon else.
It's a lovely plaice though.
Do you like the cray? Sorry, crane?
Have you used a tuna baked beans?
I can get you something to perch on.
There are three tasks in roe there.
Let minnow when it's close enough.
Oh, I've already got a haddock.
Everyone ready? Dolphinately ready?
I feel like it's time to get your skates on.
I feel a little bit tench.
Very offishal.
Don't be coy.
Not much mussel.
Warm feeling in your cockles.
I haven't got very good herring.
I've dropped the task. Not on porpoise.
Mullet over.
They've got sole.

The same series saw perhaps the greatest ever *Taskmaster* hoax, as Mark Watson was given the task of sending The Taskmaster 'a cheeky text' every day for the next six months (see TEXTS above).

This he did, with both wit and determination, especially considering several of those days were spent on Bear Grylls's Island, with no technology at his disposal. The chilling look he gave me when he discovered this was all for no points will stay with me forever.

One tricky task that didn't make it onto the television was in series 1 when my former colleague and current task consultant, Tim Key, was given this task: 'Transfer the most amount of money into The Taskmaster's bank account. Most money transferred wins.' This was inspired by the first task I ever set in the first live version of *Taskmaster* that climaxed at the Edinburgh Festival in 2010, in which the 20 comedian guinea pigs all had to put as much money into my bank account as they saw fit, giving me a grand total of £268.45 to spend on the show. Fast forward five years and we watched Tim fret for a good 15 minutes before depositing a certain sum of money that we weren't comfortable showing on television and which I don't feel ready to tell you now and which we had to return to Mr Key immediately in case his flat was repossessed.

In series 6, Tim Vine was the only person to be given TASK #157 and £50 to make an outfit outside JPS Stationers in Chesham. As expected, his outfit revolved around a pun. If yours also involves some satisfying wordplay it will absolutely be in your favour. For reference, Tim's was made out of a 'Trains 2018 Calendar'. Can you guess what he called it? The answer is here[5].

And finally, did you notice what I was wearing for only one of the contestants in series 4? She didn't. Not once.

---

[5] It was a 'track suit'. Lovely stuff as usual from Tim. In his honour, if your stationery shop is next to a mobile shop, please send me a photo. I'll pass it on. Also, for TASK #202, see TASKS #185.

ACKNOWLEDGMENTS

The first twenty people to take on tasks were my friends and fellow stand-ups at the 2010 Edinburgh Fringe. So I am forever indebted to Al Pitcher, Dan Atkinson, Guy Morgan, Henning Wehn, James Dowdeswell, Jarred Christmas, Joe Wilkinson, Josie Long, Lloyd Langford, Lloyd Woolf, Mark Olver, Mark Watson, Rick Edwards, Steve Hall, Stuart Goldsmith, Tim Fitzhigham, Tim Key, Tom Basden, Tom Wrigglesworth, and the first ever champion, Mike Wozniak. Key also deserves special mention for continuing to be an excellent Task Consultant, erratic godfather and best friend.

Since then all these people have brought the show to life and each deserves more than being merely acknowledged. So I hope the following people know how grateful I am and how highly I think of them:

Abi Heilbron, Alex Layton, Amy Rattray, Andi Meek, Andrew Dames, Anthony Dalton, Ariel Sultan, the Clapham Grand, Connor Kent, Cora McNeil, Dan Trelfer, Edd Benjamin, Ellen Green, Emilie Michell, Fountain Studios, Gary Parkhurst, James Daly, James Dillon and his team, Jane Jenkins, Jessica Reeves, Joel Porter, Jordan Livermore, Lionelle Galloppa, Maike Koch, Mark "Shirley" Owen, Mark Sangster, Martin McEwan, Neil Amor, Pete Gellatly, Peter Rowell, Pinewood Studios, Ric Clark, Sam Montague, Stevie Saponja, Tammy Cannon, Thomas Perrett, Vicky Winter. Andy Cartwright and Andy Devonshire are, of course, the greatest men.

I'd also like to thank James Taylor, Jon Thoday, Francesca Milone, Katie McKay and the whole Avalon team for their support and advice, and Hilary Rosen, Richard Watsham, Steve North and everyone at UKTV for treating me and Taskmaster like a favourite child. It has been very much appreciated. Thanks too to the team at Penguin who I'm still just getting to know but really like so far: Yvonne Jacob, Bethany Wright, Charlotte Huckle, Claire Scott, Howard Watson, Paul Simpson and Toby Clarke.

The Taskmaster himself, Greg Davies, warrants his own paragraph. He makes a truly tricky job look effortless and he's such a funny funny man to sit next to. I'm so glad you agreed to do this with me.

Finally, thanks and all the love in the world to Tom, Barney and Dara for testing tasks, suggesting solutions and inspiring everything I do, and to Rachel, for being there always on our adventures.